# THE TECHNOLOGY OF JOY

*The 101 Best Apps, Gadgets, Tools, and Supplements for Feeling More Delight in Your Life*

*By* Jonathan Robinson

**The Technology of Joy**



Author: Jonathan Robinson

Title: The Technology of Joy: *The 101 Best Apps, Gadgets, Tools and Supplements to Feel More Delight in Your Life*

Printed in the United States of America.

Design: Saravanan Ponnaiyan

First Printing: February 2016

ISBN: 978-0-692-61625-3

# ACKNOWLEDGMENT AND DEDICATION

I want to thank my various teachers, including Justin Gold, Arjuna Ardagh, Steve Forrest, Scott Catamas, Emily Orum, and my dog, Sophie. Each of you have helped show me the joys of curiosity, kindness, and experimentation.

# TABLE OF CONTENTS

Acknowledgment and Dedication iii

Introduction 1

**Chapter 1:** Exploring Your Way to Joy 5

SECTION I: Better Drugs and Supplements 15

**Chapter 2:** Colossal Cognitive Enhancers 17

**Chapter 3:** Herbal and Natural Ways to Relax 23

**Chapter 4:** Herbal and Natural Stimulant Highs 27

**Chapter 5:** The Peak Hormonal Zone 33

**Chapter 6:** Tweaking Your Neurotransmitters 37

**Chapter 7:** Micro-dosing Your Way to Nirvana 41

SECTION II: High Tech Highs 45

**Chapter 8:** Playing With Your Brainwaves 47

**Chapter 9:** Viable Virtual Reality 51

**Chapter 10:** Thyncing Your Way to Peace 55

**Chapter 11:** An Ear Clip to Unlock Your Heart 56

**Chapter 12:** Body Gadgets To Open You Up 63

**Chapter 13:** The Variety of Video Games 67

**Chapter 14:** Sounds That Meditate You 71

**Chapter 15:** Letting Your Inner Rock Star Out 75

**SECTION III:** Psychological Techniques 79

**Chapter 16:** Deep Wisdom of The Talking Stick 81

**Chapter 17:** The Full Release Method of Letting Go 85

**Chapter 18:** Three Good Things for Happiness 91

**Chapter 19:** The Number 1 Happiness Booster 95

**Chapter 20:** Tapping Towards Emotional Freedom 99

**Chapter 21:** The Spiritual Intimacy Experience 103

**Chapter 22:** The Gratitude Visit 107

**SECTION IV:** Life Enhancing Happy Apps 113

**Chapter 23:** Happify Your Blues Goodbye 117

**Chapter 24:** The Dance of Relationship Enhancement 121

**Chapter 25:** Looking for Modern Love 125

**Chapter 26:** The Attitude of Gratitude 129

**Chapter 27:** Sleeping Your Way to Success 133

**Chapter 28:** Meditation Made To Order 137

**SECTION V:** Alternative Energy Methods 141

**Chapter 29:** Orgone Accumulators and Organite 145

**Chapter 30:** Surrendering To Your Higher Power 149

**Chapter 31:** The Crystal Craze 153

**Chapter 32:** The Cheerful Chanter 157

**Chapter 33:** EMF's and Energetic Shielding 161

**Chapter 34:** The Light That Makes Things Right 165

**Chapter 35:** Give Peace a Chair 169

**SECTION VI:** The Body and Beyond 173

**Chapter 36:** Foot and Hand Massaging 175

**Chapter 37:** The Isolation Float Tank 179

**Chapter 38:** The Clarity of Aromatherapy 183

**Chapter 39:** The Infrared Sauna Experience 187

**Chapter 40:** The Tingler and Acupressure Rings 189

**Chapter 41:** Ecstatic and Five Rhythms Dance 193

**Chapter 42:** Massagers and Chi Machines 197

**Chapter 43:** Aphrodisiacs and Aphrodite 201

**SECTION VII:** Increasing Your Joy I.Q. 205

**Chapter 44:** Mixing, Matching, and Monotony 207

**Chapter 45:** How to Know if A Technology is Your Friend 211

**Chapter 46:** The Future of Joy 219

**Chapter 47:** Final Words of Advice 223

About the Author 225

# INTRODUCTION

> “The future is already here; it’s just not very evenly distributed.”
>
> *William Gibson*

"It was either an earthquake or another paradigm shift."

I popped the pink pill into my mouth and waited for the inevitable feelings of ecstasy. No, the pill wasn't the drug XTC, but rather a legal and safe alternative. Then I decided to try something new. I put on my trans-cranial stimulation device—known as the Thync, and waited to see what happened. Wow! After about five minutes, it felt like my brain was flooding me with endorphins. Finally, I placed the scalp stimulator known as the Tingler on my head. When I did this, an orgasmic wave of intense pleasure rippled through my entire body. After a few minutes of this frenzied euphoria, I took off the devices and went about my day. Having just been catapulted into sweet ecstasy, my day became both incredibly productive and happy.

This is not a future scenario. This is how I sometimes start my mornings. Nowadays, there are new and improved ways to feel good—even ecstatic—that most people *don't know* anything about. The vast majority of people find a handful of ways to feel good, and then give up the search for more ways to feel deeper joy and happiness. It's a terrible shame. In an age when depression is rampant and dangerous drug use is epidemic, amazing *new* ways to feel peaceful, euphoric, and just plain happy are popping up all over the place. However, people miss out on these amazing methods because they simply don't know about them. From safe drugs to "happy apps," to high tech brain stimulation devices, a whole new world of ways to feel good is blossoming.

In this book, I'll take you on a tour of 101 of the best and newest ways to feel fantastic—that most people are unaware of. My friends call me "Dr. Feelgood," and often laugh at my latest contrivance for feeling "high." Yet, I usually get the last laugh because once they've *tried* my latest gadget or supplement, they often ask, "So where can I get these?" It's my hope that as you read my reviews and experiences, you'll be inspired to try some of them on yourself. I'm confident that as you give a few a test ride, you'll find easy, quick, safe, low cost, and reliable new ways to feel amazing. Wouldn't that be great?

I've been a psychotherapist who has been on a forty-year quest to find the best and easiest ways to feel really wonderful. I've been on *Oprah* numerous times to talk about some of these "shortcuts to joy," and I've spoken at Google about "The Future of Happiness." Despite all the great tools available for tapping the "heaven within," I've seen many people choose ways to feel good that actually devastate their lives. If your method for feeling fantastic requires large amounts of alcohol or heroin—you're going to suffer. If your method of feeling fine involves being rich, you'll likely have to work a lot and miss out on much of life's sweetness. Therefore, it's important to explore *new* ways to feel truly wonderful that are easy to do *and* have no negative side effects.

Contrary to many people's beliefs, feeling fantastic is a worthy thing to pursue. Research shows that happy people live longer than unhappy people. They make $750,000 more over their lifetime than other folks, and are less selfish and more productive. In addition, truly joyous people raise happier kids and have a lower rate of divorce. As you find new ways to feel great, you'll likely find that your health improves, and you'll become a better partner, parent, and employee as well.

Whether you want a high tech way to cure your depression or a low-tech way to feel more joy, you'll find a way to suit your needs in my reviews of 101 different methods. But before going into my description of these amazing methods and gizmos, in Chapter One I'll describe how to evaluate what's a really good fit for you. In the final section of this book, I'll discuss how to "mix and match" these various methods, along with how to evaluate if a method is truly your "friend." Finally, I'll end with what the amazing "future of happiness" might look like, and then conclude with some final guidelines and remarks.

You need not read this book in a linear manner. If you want, find a method or section whose title looks interesting to you, and start reading. Yet, I encourage you to begin by reading the first chapter so you can better know what techniques are most likely to serve your particular needs and desires.

Inside our own body and brain, we each possess a mostly unexplored territory that contains great riches. We've heard that the "Kingdom of heaven is within," but most of us have not had the right keys to unlock this Kingdom. It is my sincere hope that some of the keys in this book will help you enjoy new and wonderful heights within your own heart, mind, body, and soul...

# CHAPTER 1

# EXPLORING YOUR WAY TO JOY

"Kids today with all their technology."

In this book, I give a description and overview of 101 of the most promising "technologies" for feeling better or feeling joyful. Technology is defined as "the application of tools and methods for achieving a specified result more efficiently." In this case, the result we're after is a better way to feel fantastic—or at the very least—a good way to overcome feeling bad. Fortunately, all the tools mentioned in this book already exist, yet most of them are not widely known or utilized. In American culture, we're bombarded with messages that say that more money or an amazing relationship is the best way to achieve happiness. Having more money or a hot date can indeed feel really good, but they both can take a long time to manifest, and they can often create new problems of their own.

The search for a new way to feel happiness or deep peace is, in my opinion, a sacred exploration and duty. Once you find a few ways that really work easily and reliably for yourself, your life is never the same. As human beings, we spend countless hours and effort *trying* to feel good. Yet, most of the ways we've been taught to feel wonderful are so difficult or ineffective that many people rarely get to enjoy prolonged joy, ecstasy, or even contentment or peace of mind.

From such a lack of experience, we tend to become more needy in our relationships, more greedy in how we live, and more dissatisfied in our lives. Look around at the world: A lot of people are in pretty bad shape, and that's partly due to the fact we're rarely in touch with our capacity for joy and deep connection. Perhaps if we had a fuller "menu" of easy ways to feel fantastic, we'd be less anxious and enjoy life more. In my own life, having a lot of ways to feel good has certainly added to the quality of my day-to-day life. Whereas I used to be a depressed young adult, nowadays I experience great joy and happiness most days of my life.

Dr. Marty Seligman, the founder of Positive Psychology, postulates that there are five "ingredients" to a truly fulfilling and happy life. He uses the acronym P.E.R.M.A. to help people remember them. They stand for Pleasure, Engagement (losing yourself in an activity), Relationships, Meaning, and Accomplishment. None of the various apps, gadgets, pills, and tools in this book can supply *all* five of those ingredients. Yet, many of the methods in this book can certainly help you get one or more of your "PERMA" needs met *very* effectively.

I believe that having a variety of ways to meet a need is better than having just a single method. For example, if your need for a caring relationship is focused on a single person, then you're in trouble if that person divorces you or dies. However, if you use some of the apps and tools described in this book to create *a lot* of caring relationships, then it's easier to feel more secure and cared for. Similarly, if your main way of experiencing pleasure is through food, you may end up overweight and miss out on a vast variety of ways to feel intense pleasure. The more ways you have to meet your "PERMA" needs, the happier and the more freedom you're likely to feel.

As a psychotherapist and workshop leader, I've noticed people often become out of balance in their approach to happiness. For example, they may pursue a lot of pleasure (the "P" in "PERMA") at the expense of having more meaning (the "M" in PERMA), or vice versa. Fortunately, the various methods in this book can help you quickly find a better balance. Whether you're looking for more Pleasure, Engagement, Relationships, Meaning, or Accomplishment, you'll find many methods here focused on *that* specific aspect of finding happiness. In fact, at the end of each chapter, I note what aspect of the PERMA formula each modality *most* satisfies. You'll find this information at the end of each chapter after the words, "Best Suited For."

In my exploration of the various ways to feel wonderful, I've seen that different things work for different people. While some people like sushi, other people hate it. In the same way, you may find a brain wave entrainment session can catapult *you* into states of ecstasy, but the same exact sounds just annoy your friends. You may also find that you and your friends desire different things from the methods you try. You may want a practice that is incredibly quick to do, while your mate's main concern may be to find a technique that helps them overcome difficult negative emotions.

Since people want different things in the techniques they try, I've come up with a list of 14 criteria to consider when choosing a particular method. By briefly going over each of these criteria, I hope it will give you a way to better evaluate what you're most interested in when trying the methods outlined in this book. For example, in my own case, I knew my general lack of discipline meant I needed to be on the lookout for a truly easy and immediately effective method. Otherwise, I'd probably be too lazy to ever use it. On the other hand, if you have no extra money to spend, you may be more on the lookout for a method that's free.

I believe that as we experience more joy and peace, our lives can become more devoted to giving to others—rather than devoted to needing more and more just to feel okay. That being said, here are 14 criteria in which to evaluate how useful any method or technology is for feeling really good. When reading this list, you might consider a couple of your favorite ways to feel great—and how many of the following criteria your method(s) satisfies:

**1. Is it easy to do?**

A first way to evaluate a method is to consider how *easy* it is to use. The average American watches over 4 hours of TV a day. Why? One reason is because, by moving their thumb a quarter of an inch, they can access

300 different entertainment options. That's pretty easy, and most people like easy. Easy to do methods are critical because few people will do methods that are complicated and hard to practice.

**2. Is it quick to do?**

I like doing yoga and meditation. Although they make me feel good, I must admit they are not quick to do. An average yoga or meditation session takes me about 45 minutes. That's why I don't do them more often. If they took only five minutes to do, I'm sure I'd do them every single day. That's why methods that take five minutes to do (or less) can be especially valuable. When a method takes five minutes or less, there's a greater likelihood that you'll actually use it more often.

**3. Is the method effective and/or powerful for you?**

I have a friend who uses a method known as EFT, or better known as "tapping." (See Chapter 20). He swears by the method, and it's a very elegant technique. I like everything about it except for one thing—it doesn't seem to work for me. When evaluating a method, more important than anything else is whether the method actually works for *you*. You can't rely on other people's accounts to know if something will work for you. You have to try it. Yet, once you find a method that really rocks your world, you have a friend for life.

**4. Is the method free from negative side effects?**

In Chapter 45, "How to Know if a Technology is Your Friend," I explore how various methods have subtle negative side effects. For example, you can become overly addicted to a technique to feel better (think video games), or find that if you *don't* use a method every day, you end up feeling like crap (think caffeine). Ultimately, you want to choose methods that don't create their own set of problems.

**5. Is the method versatile or can it be used on any issue?**

I like to dance. Dancing feels good, but it's not very good at helping a person process stuck feelings from their past. Nor will it, in most cases, help a person to resolve their addiction problems. Some techniques are just very adaptable to helping you overcome the challenges you have in life, and some methods are simply good for a very specific purpose or goal.

**6. Is it free or low cost?**

I'm a cheapskate. If a method costs a bunch of money every time I use it, I will tend not to use it very often. Except for my spa (which I love), most of the ways I have for feeling great are low cost or free. Yet, for those of you who have plenty of money, I will review a couple of amazing gadgets that can definitely be worth a test ride!

**7. Is the method invisible to others?**

If possible, you want to be able to use any method for feeling good in as many places and situations as possible. If your method for feeling fantastic involves wearing funny electrodes on your head, or jumping up and down, it will be hard to do that technique in the office. Therefore, methods that can be done without other people's knowledge (or disapproving looks) are the most practical.

**8. Can it be done anywhere?**

As I mentioned before, yoga and meditation are great methods, but they can't be done in your car, and they can't be done while talking to a friend. Fortunately, some of the techniques in this book actually *can* be done in almost any place or situation. That can be good to know the next time you have a meltdown in your office—or your car.

**9. Does it deal with a root issue?**

We all have "baggage" or issues that mostly derive from our childhood wounding. When we fail to be aware of these issues, they can cause much damage to our life and our relationships. Traditionally, people have gone to psychotherapists to handle such inner baggage, but that is not always the best way to handle such things. Some methods outlined in this book can actually be very effective in routing out and dismantling one's neurotic tendencies. On the other hand, some methods are clearly not geared to "work" on such deep-seated stuff. However, if you *do* want to be able to do "self-therapy," it's good to know if the method you select is effective in that arena.

**10. Does it work on your body, mind, and emotions?**

Some apps, gadgets, and tools are focused exclusively on the mind, some on the body, and some on one's emotions. Occasionally, you'll find a method that actually works on all three modalities at the same time. Such techniques can be an added benefit since they are working in a balanced and efficient manner.

**11. Does the method improve with practice?**

It feels good to get better at something, and that holds true with "inner technology" as well. With certain methods, such as taking drugs or supplements to alter your consciousness, you generally don't get "better" with practice. In fact, the more you take it, the less likely it will have its same powerful effect. On the other hand, there are methods that don't feel so great the first few times you use them, yet over time they become easier, more powerful, and quicker to use. Such practices are important to be aware of since they tend to be really good for you (such as meditation and yoga).

### 12. Can it be used to help others?

As a psychotherapist, I'm always on the lookout for tools that I can use with my clients. Also, as a person interested in helping friends through a hard time, I like to "collect" methods that can quickly be used to help folks. Certain techniques can easily be modified to be used "on" someone else, while others are not so adaptable.

### 13. Does it lead to emotional or spiritual maturity?

In Chapter 45, my friend and fellow writer, Arjuna Ardagh and I discuss how to know if a certain technology is your "friend." By "friend," we mean does it ultimately point you in a direction that is in line with your values, and is healthy and admirable. Upon a first try, heroin may *feel* like a friend—but most people know it does not lead to emotional or spiritual maturity. Some practices, such as meditation, have been shown to have dozens of beneficial effects on one's life, while others are more focused on being a quick and useful distraction. When choosing a technique, it's good to know the difference.

### 14. Is it easy to learn?

My wife, like me, is also a psychotherapist. In the last few years, she has extensively studied a method called EMDR. This has been shown to be very effective in helping people overcome deep-seated trauma and other psychological issues. Although it is quite effective, I don't use it. The reason? It takes dozens of hours of precise training to get good at. If you're like me, you may prefer techniques that can be learned in a single session—or maybe two. Those practices don't have a high "entry price," and therefore are easier to explore and try.

Besides knowing the many ways to evaluate a method, it's helpful to consider what it is *you* most need—or what it is you would most enjoy. For example, as a therapist, I get paid to help people. Therefore,

I highly value methods that fulfill criteria #12—they can be used to help others. If that's not your interest, you need not explore methods whose main attribute is their helpful effect on other people. Likewise, because I'm very busy, I'm partial to methods that can be done in under three minutes. However, if you have plenty of time on your hands, the "quickness" of a method is less relevant to your needs.

While reading the descriptions of various methods in this book, you may get a sense if a particular method is a good match for you. However, it can sometimes be hard to know until you actually *try* them out. After all, you may have had the experience of hearing a description of a certain *person* that sounded wonderful, only to find that your experience of that actual person fell far short of your expectations. Therefore, whenever possible I'll briefly describe *my* experience with each method, but remember that my experience may be totally different than yours. Ultimately, you'll have to try a method out for yourself if you truly want to know how effective it is for you.

Since I've written this book largely to help match you with suitable methods, I've come up with a simple system to help you determine this quickly and easily. At the end of each chapter, I suggest the "Best Features" of each method in terms of the 14 criteria I just mentioned. I also list what I think are a couple of the "Possible Shortcomings" for each modality—when measured by the 14 criteria of a really good method. These quick summaries, along with my classifying methods as helpful in one or more ways of increasing "PERMA" (Pleasure, Engagement, Relationships, Meaning, and Accomplishment), should help you select methods that immediately suit your needs and desires. May you enjoy your explorations!

SECTION ONE

# BETTER DRUGS AND SUPPLEMENTS

"Take the green pill to feel hunky, the yellow pill to feel dory."

Americans spend about $330 *billion* dollars on prescription medications each year, and another $100 billion on illegal drugs. In addition, Americans spend $21 billion more dollars on vitamins and supplements. That's a lot of money. With monetary incentives like that, the search for better drugs and supplements is extremely well financed. It's just a matter of time before we invent mind-altering drugs with even greater power and less negative side effects. In fact, even today there are some legal drugs and supplements—that most people don't know about—that can truly knock your socks off.

In 1984, I was a graduate student in psychology studying the therapeutic effects of a drug known as MDMA, now better known as XTC. At the time, my research indicated you could do a year of therapy in one day with the use of this drug. Of course, when teens started abusing this drug, it was made illegal. Yet recently, new government sponsored research has shown that MDMA can be very effective for treating Post Traumatic Stress Syndrome and other disorders. In a similar vein, new research is showing that illegal drugs such as marijuana, LSD, Ketamine, and Psilocybin mushrooms all have clear therapeutic potential. It's just a matter of time before these drugs are used even more for increasing joy and decreasing disorders such as depression.

Along with the explosion of legal and illegal drug use, the field of vitamin and herbal supplementation has taken off in recent years. Many of my friends and I regularly alter our mood through the use of various "smart pills," and legal supplements that mimic the effects of XTC, alcohol, and marijuana. Having been an avid follower of such supplementation, I have been impressed with how much better they are getting over the last few years. In this section, I will discuss some of my personal favorites, and give you information on their uses, potential abuses, and how you can easily purchase them.

# CHAPTER 2

# COLOSSAL COGNITIVE ENHANCERS

In the early 1990's, a book came out called *Smart Drugs and Nutrients*. This book suggested that, with the right supplementation, a person could become smarter and more productive. At the time, the suggested supplementation was not very effective, but as with all technologies, it keeps getting better. Since then, the field has exploded. Of course, most people are aware of various energy drinks that can kick your body and brain into high gear. Yet, these mostly caffeinated beverages take a toll on the body and only work for some people. Fortunately, there are now a lot of cognitive enhancing options, often called "nootropics," to choose from.

The term "cognitive enhancer" or "nootropics" denotes any supplement that has the potential to increase mental alertness, intelligence, focus, and/or clarity of mind. If you ever saw the movie or TV show, *Limitless*, you can understand the possibilities inherent in such a product. Caffeine is the most popular drug in the world—partly because it makes you more mentally alert with minimal negative side effects. Yet, nowadays there are many cognitive enhancing supplements you can buy at your health food store or online. All you need is some money, some time to explore, and an open mind.

First, the bad news. I will make many recommendations in this chapter, but you should know that people react very differently to many of these supplements. I suggest that, when possible, you buy and try a very small amount of any of these pills and see what effect they have on you. Only by trying them out will you know exactly what they do for you. In addition, people vary a lot in terms of the *amount* of each drug or supplement that is the right dose for them. Case in point: When I drink coffee (which is rare), a full cup sends me on a wild emotional roller coaster for about 12 hours. On the other hand, some people drink 5 cups a day and barely register any effect. In general, start out conservatively and then if nothing happens, you can always take more.

Now the good news. There are many great, safe, and legal cognitive enhancers to choose from. I'll mention many of my favorites, along with websites where you can purchase them. Yet, since there are so many, I suggest you Google "cognitive enhancers" or go to the websites I suggest and do some research on your own. There are two cognitive enhancers in the "racetam" class I especially like. One is called "Aniracetam," and the other is called "Pramiracetam." Aniracetam is shorter acting, but may be better at improving one's mood, whereas Pramiracetam is longer acting, and more powerful when it comes to creating mental focus. You can buy both of these on many websites, including www.absorbyourhealth.com. It's best to try a small amount of each to see which one you might like better. If you want to buy samples of several of these types of cognitive enhancers to see which work best for you, you can go to http://smbnootropics.com/collections/smart-size-nootropic-samplers. Also, a good guide to learn more about these supplements can be found on www.smarternootropics.com. Once there, click on the free "The Complete Guide to Nootropics."

As I mentioned before, people react differently to these pills. While they are considered safe, some people don't feel them right away. Especially with Pramiracetam, you may have to take it for up to a week to feel its full effect. There is also some evidence that their effect is increased if taken in conjunction with 300 to 600 mg of CDP choline, or an Omega 3 supplement. I've enjoyed both. I find I can really focus better with either of them, and they can often help get me into "the zone" where my mind is both quiet and clear. Try them if you have the money and see what they can do for you.

Next, I want to discuss the wonders of Adrafinil. This is a supplement that turns into Modafinil once ingested in your body. Modafinil is a prescription medication the army uses to keep soldiers incredibly alert and focused for long periods of time. Adrafinil is non-prescription, but also works quite well. My personal experience with both of these pills is rather intense. If I want to stay focused and alert for 12 hours, I take a half dose of Modafinil or 300 mg of Adrafinil. If I want to simply be at my best throughout the day, I might take half as much of either. Taking a supplement called Phenibut (250 to 500 mg) can be a nice addition to Adrafinil. When I needed to write 30 pages in a day for a book I was doing, I found that taking some Adrafinil and Phenibut made the job easy—and I had a great time doing it. Adrafinil is available for sale online, but don't take it more than once or twice a week.

If you're looking for one tablet that does it all, you might try Sulbutiamine. Sulbutiamine is a lipid soluble form of vitamin B-1 which can cross the blood brain barrier more easily. It has been shown to improve motivation, focus, memory and mood. Wow! I love this stuff. About three times a week (tolerance builds quickly) I take two 200 mg pills of a Sulbutiamine supplement from Double Wood Supplements. After taking it I feel focused, energized, and truly joyous. Your experience may vary, but if it doesn't vary by much, you'll be thanking me for the rest of your life. In addition, it's relatively inexpensive and considered healthy for you unless you take it every day. It's definitely worth a test ride. If you want to turbo charge this vitamin for the brain even more, consider taking 750 mg Aniracetam with it, and/or 500 mg of CDP Choline with it—along with some food. Currently this is my favorite combination for feeling focused, motivated, and happy.

If cost is a big factor for you, you can get supplements such as phosphatidyl choline or DMAE at Vitacost.com for very little money. My experience with these pills is that they are much more subtle than the others I've mentioned so far. However, both of these products are considered to be perfectly safe long term, and have been shown to have cognitive enhancing abilities if taken regularly. By the way, I have no financial arrangement with any of the companies I recommend. My motivation in recommending certain online sites is simply to help you gain more information and/or find these products at a reliable and inexpensive source.

Finally, I want to recommend www.webnutrients.com. This site has many innovative products of the cognitive and mood enhancing type that you can easily purchase. In fact, by filling out their online questionnaire, you can have your pills tailor made to meet your exact needs and desires. They have something called "Happy Caps" that indeed affect your mind and mood, "Real NZT" that's a wild mental ride, and my favorite, a tube of five capsules called "Noostax" that both gives me focus and blisses me out for about eight hours. If you're interested in the field of cognitive enhancing pills, this site is worth checking out. At the navigation bar, click on "order" to see the full range of products they offer. Yet, know that you will have to go through a trial and error period to know what dosage and what pills work best for you.

If money is not a major limiting factor for you, there's some new stuff always coming out that many consider the "Cadillac" of cognitive enhancers and dementia preventers. The website, http://ForrestHealth.com has a lot of the latest and greatest brain supplements. I would recommend Brain Vital and Brain Vibrant Supreme, but Phos Cal 900, or Energy 1 and Energy 2 sprays are also worth checking out.

Lastly, I'll talk about an old favorite—caffeine. The biggest problem with caffeine is the tendency towards developing a quick tolerance. Yet, if you know of other options for energy and focus beyond a cup of coffee, you can vary your supplementation so you don't develop such a quick tolerance for caffeine. If caffeine can make you jittery, consider downing your coffee or energy drink with a supplement known as L-theanine. A lot of people report that the combo of caffeine and 200 mg of L-theanine is a nice, smooth, energetic ride without the caffeine crash at the end.

Rather than give you a thorough data dump of all the cognitive enhancers out there, my aim has been to introduce you to this fast developing and exciting field. Hopefully the information I supplied here is enough to give you a direction and starting point. Yet, if these pills intrigue you, start by buying a small amount and see how it goes for you. You can even "mix and match" until you find a combination that seems to really suit your needs. Once you find some pills that seem to have a truly positive effect on your mood and focus, and are also devoid of negative side effects, you got a friend for life.

**Best Suited** for improving your Engagement, Pleasure, and Accomplishment.

**Best Features**: Ease of use, quickness, powerful effect, can be done anywhere, and not visible to others.

**Possible Shortcomings**: Can have unpleasant negative side effects, cost, doesn't deal with your issues, and does not improve with practice.

# CHAPTER 3

# HERBAL AND NATURAL WAYS TO RELAX

I live in a small town. When I lecture or lead workshops, I fly into various cities. The first thing that always strikes me when I go to a big city is how *tense* everyone looks. Between the noise and the constant sense of always needing to be in a hurry, very few people look calm and relaxed. People are often so "wound up" that it's only when they take a vacation or get a massage that they realize how uptight they were. Fortunately, there are a lot of good natural pills and tinctures you can buy to aid in relaxing and letting go. In this chapter, I'll offer my opinion about several of my favorites.

Before describing various tinctures and pills, I want to list the popular cultural methods for letting go and relaxing: alcohol and marijuana. Both of these drugs can be a fine way to relax. In fact, each of them have been shown to potentially have health benefits when taken in moderation. Yet, we all know people who have become either psychologically or physically addicted to one of these drugs. If alcohol or marijuana work for you, then great. But if they don't, or if you want more variety in how you relax, then the following remedies will be of great interest.

Many years ago I went to Fiji and spent many a night drinking "kava." Kava comes from a root of a plant, and in moderation is considered quite safe. Unfortunately, it tastes a lot like dirt, and you need to drink a lot of it to feel its relaxing, somewhat alcohol-like properties. Luckily, modern day business has come to the rescue and if you want to get high on Kava, it's as easy as downing some quality Kava tincture. My personal favorite is "Kava Liquid Extract Vanuatu's Finest." The bottle says to take 30 drops, but at first you'll likely need more. When you are familiar with its effects after a few tries, it won't take as much to feel what it does. You can buy a bottle at TwistedThistleApothecary.com (hereby referred to as TTA). They also do mail orders by calling them at (510) 644-3727.

While you're shopping or checking out stuff at TTA, you might want to give their Mucuna powder and Kratom a try. Mucuna is derived from vines and shrubs in tropical climates. It also tastes like dirt, but its effects are mild euphoria and a good mood. You can start out with a teaspoon hidden in some applesauce—to hide the taste. If you don't feel anything, try 1.5 teaspoons. One of the properties of Mucuna is that it increases your dopamine levels—one of our major feel good neurotransmitters. In fact, you can buy Mucuna daily supplements if you notice that you like its effects.

Kratom is a subject one can spend many moons discussing. It is derived from a tree in the coffee family. Its leaves have long been used for uplifting mood and treating health problems. As with marijuana, there are many different types of Kratom and they each have their own unique effects. If you call the fine folks at TTA, or visit their website, they will go over the various effects of the Kratom products they sell. Perhaps my personal favorite is one called "Wooly Mammoth." It leads to a mild, relaxing euphoria that can last for several hours. It's important to know that you don't want to mix Kratom with alcohol. I don't know why, but everyone always says that. You've been warned.

Venturing on, a product known as Gabatrol is definitely worth a mention. According to their website, www.Gabatrol.com, "Gabatrol optimizes brain function in several ways. One such way is via GABA, a naturally occurring amino acid found in food, but which is also a potent neurotransmitter in the brain. By enhancing GABA levels in the brain, Gabatrol promotes relaxation and relief from feelings of stress and anxiety. Gabatrol also helps optimal brain chemistry by increasing the other "feel good" neurotransmitters like Serotonin and Dopamine."

A friend of mine suggested I take eight Gabatrol pills at once—perhaps because that's what worked for him. I spent the next three days in a completely relaxed, semi-stupor state. It was a bit much. I suggest you take the recommended two or three pills, and if you don't notice anything, try more on another day. Of course, if you want to walk around in a relaxed, semi-stupor state, eight pills should do the trick.

Recently, a friend of mine turned me on to a bottle of something called "Mood Shine." If you'd like to avoid alcohol, but you like feeling a bit tipsy, this concoction can be your thing. It's a mixture of Kratom with some other nifty herbs, and it left me feeling happy, euphoric, and no noticeable hangover the next day. You can find out more at www.Brilliant-Elixirs.com.

Last, but not least, if tinctures are your thing, you can find a whole lot of them at www.harmonyherbals.net. If you're looking to chill, I can recommend their "Joy," and their "Damiana" blends. The good thing about these blends is that they are easy on the body and they don't last long. The bad thing about them is that their effect doesn't last long. I guess it depends on how long you have to chill.

Since I have some extra money and I like to explore, I've tried all these products and found the ones that I like the most. I wish I could say, "Product X always works for people," but I can't. People react differently to the same drugs, and they react even more uniquely to herbal-based tinctures and pills. Yet, if you try a bunch of stuff, you'll surely find some goods that really *do it* for you. Since relaxing and feeling euphoric are two of the finer gifts in life, it can be worth doing a bit of experimentation.

**Best Suited** for increasing Pleasure, Engagement, and Relationships.

**Best Features:** Easy to use, can be done anywhere, and can affect the body, mind, and emotions.

**Possible Shortcomings:** Mild effect, cost, and can lead to unpleasant side effects for some people.

## CHAPTER 4

# HERBAL AND NATURAL STIMULANT HIGHS

Caffeine is currently the most popular drug on Earth. Why is that? Well, it satisfies many of the criteria I've talked about throughout this book for being a good method. It's easy, quick, effective, and it has few negative side effects. In addition, studies show that moderate consumption of caffeine in the form of coffee can even help prevent several types of cancer. Impressive. Yet, it does have a serious Achilles heel. If you drink coffee or take caffeine regularly, you develop a tolerance to it. It becomes less effective in supplying you with a boost of energy. Furthermore, it can lead to a "crash" at the end, it taxes your adrenal glands, and it can keep you awake at night.

Fortunately, if you're looking for a consistent boost of energy or even a stimulating "high," there are many herbal and natural energy products out there that you can use. Since people react very differently to these types of products, you'll have to do some experimentation. Yet, your explorations can be well worth it. I have five different energy products I use on a regular basis. Because I don't take the same ones over and over, my body never creates a tolerance to any of them.

If I need to get a lot done in a given day, or if I just want to feel a bit high and more alert than usual, I can choose from an assortment of goodies that reliably make me feel energized and fantastic. Sometimes I feel like Popeye with a can of spinach. By popping the right pill in my mouth, I can conquer the deepest challenges with ease—while actually nourishing my body with supplements that are healthy.

In this chapter, I will review six of my favorite energy boosters that are generally considered healthy. In Chapter Two (Colossal Cognitive Enhancers), I already reviewed some of my favorite ways to be mentally alert. Since our body and mind are intimately connected (on our good days), there is a lot of overlap between stimulants that affect the mind and body. I suggest you take some time to experiment with any of the products I describe, being careful to start with a low dose. Finding the exact right dose is important. The first time I took a product I like called "Uptime," I took the recommended amount according to the bottle. Sixteen hours later, I was still flying high and couldn't get to sleep. The next time I took some Uptime, I tried half that amount. I found this reduced dosage led to a smooth, good feeling ride with no negative side effects. Your mileage may vary.

Anyway, here's the best of what I think is out there and worth exploring:

**Uptime:** As I mentioned, this nifty pill is effective, healthy, and can pack a wallop. It has some caffeine in it, but it mitigates the tendency for a caffeine crash by putting the caffeine in a healthy blend of vitamins, algae, wheat grass, and alfalfa leaf. In addition, on www.Up-time.com, you can also order a maximum energy blend and various energy drinks. My body likes this stuff.

**Energy Now Ginseng**: These pills get incredibly rave reviews at Amazon.com, and for good reason. They supply a good balance of lasting mental and physical energy that feels great. It does have some Guarana—which is basically caffeine—so you can build a tolerance to it after a while. Yet, the formula includes ginseng and other healthy herbs that keep you from getting the jitters or crashing at the end. As with Uptime, they recommend you take all three pills in the packet. Yet, if you're sensitive to stimulants, you might try one at a time. You can always take a second pill an hour later, and even a third pill later in the day. That way, you can experience all day energy—instead of the typical high and crash of many other energy products.

**Ultra Energy Plus**: This product is a bit different than most energy pills. It does not supply a "rush" of energy. It contains no caffeine, guarana, or other caffeine like stimulants. Rather, on its website, www.RainbowLight.com, this product is described as providing "Stimulant-free support for natural, balanced energy with a unique combination of herbs featuring schissandra and codonopsis with superfoods of bee pollen, spirulina, wheat grass, (and) barley grass." This is a great product if you are too sensitive to caffeine, or don't want to ingest anything that may eventually tax your body. It takes a while to notice its subtle, but healthy feeling effects. On the other hand, the ingredients it contains provide your body with ongoing nutritional support.

**5 Hour Energy**: Unless you've been living in a cave, you've probably seen the little bottles of "5 Hour Energy" at your local supermarket or convenience store. These little bottles do a quite a good job—as long as you're okay with a fair amount of caffeine. Like with Uptime, 5 Hour Energy blends a bunch of good brain nutrients in—thus helping you maintain alertness and avoid a crash. The main downside of this product is that it's more expensive than Uptime, but an upside is you can find it almost anywhere. If you're sensitive to caffeine, you might want to try half a bottle. The first time I tried it, I downed the whole bottle—which was a mistake. Yet, I came up with a catchy new name for it—"12 Hour Holy Mother of God Energy." I guess I'm more sensitive than most.

**Noostax Capsules:** In Chapter Two, I briefly mentioned a product from a company named webnuturients.com called NZT-48. NZT-48 is a powerful brain and body stimulator, but it's a powder—and I don't generally want to hassle with powders. Yet, at the same website, they sell a product called "Noostax Capsules." After filling out their brief online questionnaire, webnutrients.com sends you tubes filled with five *custom made* capsules geared towards creating the exact effect you're looking for. These five capsules per day will cost you about $5 per trip, but I can guarantee you they will be a wild mental and emotional rocket ship ride. If you've ever taken the drug XTC, these capsules can be a lot like that—but without the illegality, body burden, or next day hangover. You can find out more by clicking on "order" from their home page, and scrolling down to "Noostax."

**Chocamine:** Finally, I want to offer a little known stimulant and mood booster that is made up of cacao. Cacao is like cocoa, but much healthier. In fact, it's been shown to increase longevity in mammals and have a host of other health benefits—like lowering blood pressure. In concentrated form, it can give people both energy and a mood lift. I recommend getting it at www.TwistedThistleApothecary.com, where their Chocamine powder is made up of a 25x extract of cacao. Start with a half teaspoon in a drink to start, and if you don't feel anything, you can slowly try some more. It's always nice when what you use to feel good and energized has the "side effect" of also being good for you.

It takes time and some money to experiment with all the possibilities here. Yet, once you find the products you like, you'll find that you're both more productive and happier. By having several energy boosters that work for you, you can avoid the problem of diminishing returns and taxing your body in unhealthy ways. The result is something akin to a superpower—an ability to be at your best consistently, day in and day out.

**Best Suited** for increasing Engagement, Accomplishment, and Pleasure.

**Best Features:** Easy to use, quickness and power of effect, not visible, can affect body, mind and emotions, and can be done anywhere.

**Possible Shortcomings**: Can have negative side effects for some, cost, doesn't help with personal issues, and does not improve with practice.

## CHAPTER 5

# THE PEAK HORMONAL ZONE

As I step into the controversial area known as Hormone Replacement Therapy (HRT), I must mention that I am not a doctor. Therefore, you should take everything I say with a grain of salt—and if you're considering HRT, be sure to consult your doctor. That being said, I can share with you what I've read on the web, as well as my personal experience and the experience of several friends who have tried HRT. Also, doctors don't agree on any of this stuff either, so depending on which doctor you ask, you'll get totally different advice.

Hormone Replacement Therapy (HRT) used to be primarily for middle-aged men or women who were attempting to counteract a deficiency in their hormone levels. For men, this meant trying to get their "Low T" or testosterone levels back up to par. For women, this usually meant counteracting the effects of menopause by taking synthetic or bio-identical hormones of estrogen and progesterone. Then, people slowly discovered that they felt better after taking these hormones. Often their mood improved, and even their bodies got stronger. Big Pharma was more than happy to market the idea that just about everyone could benefit from HRT. So the controversy began.

If you go to your doctor, you can get a blood test to determine if you might benefit from more testosterone (if you're a man), or estrogen and progesterone (if you're a woman). Technically, you need a prescription to get these hormones—which is a good thing because they do come with health risks. HRT includes an increased risk of heart disease, breast cancer, and stroke—among other things. But in a day and age of "Internet prescription drugs," many people try HRT without a doctor's close supervision. They've heard of the potential mood and body improvements that come with HRT, and so they take their chances.

Because I'm a bit reckless, I got me some testosterone cream to see what effect it would have on me. First, I got a blood test to determine if my testosterone level was low. It was normal for a man of my age—I'm 56. As I put the cream on every day, I noticed I felt a bit more aggressive—like when I was driving or when playing tennis. Of course, it could have been the placebo effect. I didn't notice any big mood enhancement, so after a month I stopped taking it.

For men who have "Low T," I often hear a different type of story. Several friends have reported that once they started taking testosterone, they felt much better, had more energy, and their sex life dramatically improved. Therefore, if you're a middle aged man and are feeling a bit listless, getting a blood test to see if you might need HRT can be a worthwhile thing to find out.

As for women, all I can say is what I hear. I've known women who say HRT saved them from menopausal depression. One woman I know said she actually took low levels of *testosterone* to feel better. Not long ago, I had lunch with her and she looked depressed. Normally, I knew her as a happy and high-energy person, so I asked her, "What's going on?" She said, "I ran out of my testosterone prescription." According to her, it was her lack of a small amount of testosterone that made the difference between a life of enjoyment and a life of depression.

If you dive into the thicket of whether women who are menopausal should be taking HRT, you're in for quite a dizzying ride. HRT has been shown to be effective in treating depression for women caused by menopause, but it also carries significant risks. The research is ongoing and, frankly, changes every few months. Therefore it's best to talk to your doctor and decide what might be right for you.

In conclusion, HRT for men or women is medically controversial. Testosterone drops by 1 to 1.5% per year for men—beginning around age forty. For men with low levels of testosterone, supplementation has been shown to increase mood, muscle mass, sexual desire and strength. Yet, it does come with risks. And in case you think you can boost your testosterone naturally, none of those "boosters" you see in ads have actually been shown to work in placebo controlled studies. When it comes to women, HRT for menopause is a bit more medically accepted, but still controversial. If you think it might be right for you, discuss it with your doctor. In some cases, the right amount of hormonal supplementation can make a world of difference.

**Best Suited** for increasing Relationships and Accomplishment.

**Best Features:** Easy to use, not visible to others, can affect the body, mind, and emotions.

**Possible Shortcomings:** Can have negative side effects, cost, does not improve with practice, and can mask underlying issues.

# CHAPTER 6

# TWEAKING YOUR NEUROTRANSMITTERS

Reported clinical depression is up by 500% in the last 50 years. In addition, there are many new "brain disorders" that seem to be thriving—such as ADD, and chronic irritability and stress. While the causes for such disorders are many and varied, a unique new way to treat them is simple: find out how your brain's neurotransmitters are doing, and if they are out of balance, take supplements to balance them out.

When doctors take a blood sample from you, they're basically checking to see how various bio-markers compare to healthy people. If something is "out of whack," they generally prescribe pills to help restore you to a healthy level. Well, finding out your neurotransmitter levels is basically the same idea. When you purchase a neurotransmitter test, you get a test kit mailed to your home. In the kit are instructions for sending back a saliva and urine sample to the test lab. Soon, you'll be sent a report that indicates how your brain's neurotransmitters compare to healthy adults your age.

If your neurotransmitters are not in their proper "balance," the report will provide you with recommended supplements you can take to restore your balance. For example, if your levels of dopamine are low, the lab tests recommend that you take the supplement known as Macuna. By taking this supplement daily, your dopamine (and your level of pleasure) is likely to go way up.

It is unfortunate that this common sense way of dealing with depression—or a loss of pleasure—is not more popular. Doctors are told such tests are not necessary because Prozac or Ritalin can simply be prescribed for depression or ADD. Yet, tinkering with the brain is not a good idea until you know exactly what might be "off." It would be crazy for a doctor to say, "You need an iron supplement," before he or she saw your blood panel. Likewise, it's unwise to take a drug—such as Prozac—before knowing if your serotonin supply is out of balance.

There are many websites and labs that will do basic neurotransmitter tests. One outfit I like is www.ForrestHealth.com where you can type in "neurotransmitter tests" in the search bar and get a variety of tests to choose from. They range from a "neuroscreen basic test" for $247.00 to more expensive and advanced tests. When the test results come back, you'll be given recommendations for supplements to take to help you get back into the normal range.

Most people who take the test receive a recommendation to take between one and three supplements to help balance out their neurotransmitters. While recommendations vary, a typical scenario might be to take the supplements for three to six months and see how things change. Then, maybe a year later, take another test and see if you're fully in the normal range—pretty much like how a person takes an annual blood test.

From the research I did, I heard that many people report dramatic results from this approach to feeling good. If your neurotransmitters are out of whack, you might try therapy, exercise, or dozens of other modalities for feeling better—with little results. That's why it makes sense to find out what may be *physically* causing you a problem before you research more psychological or metaphysical explanations. Your brain is by far your most important organ when it comes to feeling joy and overall health. Checking "under the hood" to see what's going on there by taking neuroscreening tests is a good place to start.

**Best Suited** for increasing Pleasure, Engagement, and Relationships.

**Best Features**: Can be powerful, can deal with "root" issues, can benefit the body, mind and emotions, and is not visible to others.

**Possible Shortcomings:** Cost, and can take a while to "work."

# CHAPTER 7

# MICRO-DOSING YOUR WAY TO NIRVANA

In my freshman year at UCLA, I got to intern with a man named Dr. Sidney Cohen. At the time, Dr. Cohen was the only person in America who was allowed by the U.S. government to give LSD to volunteers. In the 1960's, Dr. Timothy Leary gave out LSD to college students at Harvard, and was subsequently fired for his actions. After that fiasco, the U.S. government put a tight lid on any LSD research—despite promising results on how LSD can be very beneficial to certain populations. I was fortunate enough to learn from Dr. Cohen that LSD was not just a "mind-blowing" 60's trip, but was also a potentially valuable aid to spiritual maturity.

During my college years, I occasionally experimented with LSD and "magic" psilocybin mushrooms. I always had inspiring experiences in those explorations. In fact, my experiences with these drugs led me to start a daily meditation practice and led me to seek out spiritual teachers and spiritual communities. For several decades I pursued anything that I thought could help me reenact these "highs" without actually ingesting a drug.

Then, about four years ago, I came upon a book by James Fadiman, an early researcher of LSD and other hallucinogenic drugs. In his book, *The Psychedelic Explorer's Guide*, Fadiman talked about people who regularly take a "micro dose" or very small amount of LSD—and then proceed to go about their normal day. The idea intrigued me. According to the reports of people he interviewed, virtually everyone who ingested about 10 micrograms of LSD (about 1/15$^{th}$ of a normal dose) found it to be very enjoyable. In addition, the people he interviewed commonly reported that it was also helpful for spiritual learning and even made them more effective in their job and their relationships. Furthermore, no one reported any negative side effects from such experiences, even if they were taking it two or three times a week.

First, I need to say that LSD and psilocybin mushrooms are still illegal, and I am not advocating their use. I am only sharing my personal experiences so you can be aware of new possibilities. All of my own experiences with micro-dosing with LSD or psilocybin have been truly wonderful. I typically take it in the morning and then go about my normal day. Often, I forget I took anything, but I just feel a bit happier, more peaceful, more present, and more heart oriented than I normally am. People I interact with don't think I'm "high," but sometimes they'll comment that I seem "really peaceful or caring today." In a very real way, micro-dosing has shown me what I would be like if I weren't so caught up in my neurotic mind. Having had such "fore visions" of deep spiritual peace, I've been inspired to re commit to my spiritual practices so I can become more peaceful without the drugs.

While "micro-dosing" is a relatively new concept in the West, it has been used for thousands of years by indigenous cultures who have experimented with hallucinogenic plants and mushrooms in small doses. While there has been virtually zero research done on its long-term safety, I could not find any reported problems associated with it in the literature. Dr. Albert Hoffman, the discoverer of LSD was reported to regularly micro-dose with LSD, and he lived to be a mentally sharp 101 year-old man!

For those who might consider experimenting in this arena, I have a few pieces of advice. First, start conservatively. You can always increase the amount that you take, but you can't decrease what you've already taken. Second, try having a normal day while on a micro dose. Hopefully, this will help you to better see how you usually live a normal day, and how you might be different if you were just a bit more present. Finally, be discrete with who you tell about micro-dosing. If you truly are taking a very small dose, your behavior changes should not be particularly noticeable to those you interact with. You may have to experiment with what is exactly the right "micro-dose" for you.

Besides taking small amounts of psilocybin mushrooms or LSD, many people also try to have a normal day while on other drugs. In the last twenty years, millions of people (including children) are using small amounts of drugs such as Ritalin or Adderall for ADHD, marijuana for fun or pain control, and other drugs for various purposes. Of course, the opportunities for abuse are large, yet so are the opportunities for life enhancement.

From my own experimentation, as well as what I've seen in friends and clients, I've learned that trial and error is part of the process of discovering what works for you. In my experience, not even a psychiatrist can know what drugs will work for an individual, and what drugs will not. However, if you are willing to do some experimentation on yourself, you may find some forms of micro-dosing that dramatically enhance your life.

**Best Suited** for improving your Meaning, Engagement, Pleasure, and Relationships.

**Best Features:** Easy to use, can help with any issue, invisible, low cost, can be done anywhere, can lead to greater maturity, and can affect body, mind and emotions.

**Possible Shortcomings:** For some people it can have negative side effects and it does not tend to improve with practice. In addition, LSD is illegal.

## SECTION TWO

# HIGH TECH HIGHS

**"Still no improvement? Nurse, attach more gizmos."**

Moore's Law states that every two years or so, you can put twice as many transistors on a microchip. This has led to an exponential explosion of technology during the last 50 years. As various technologies get better and better, some of them have immense implications for how we entertain ourselves and seek happiness. For example, nowadays people spend a lot of time playing games on their smartphones, finding love online, and spending time on sites such as Facebook. None of these things even existed twenty years ago.

At a talk I did at Google in 2014, titled "The Future of Happiness," I discussed various futuristic ways technology will impact our search for happiness. You can find that talk at this link: https://www.youtube.com/watch?v=i2WC00LvGAo., or better yet, type in "Jonathan Robinson + Google talk" in the search bar and it will come up. Anyway, although that talk was just 18 months ago, some of the "science fiction" methods I presented have already come to pass. In this section, I'll discuss several of what I consider the most promising high tech highs. While some of these methods are currently rather crude and costly, technology has a way of creeping up on you and becoming really good and very cheap quite quickly. What may now involve costly brain surgery may—five years from now—involve something like a quick visit to your doctor. Once some of these methods are perfected, there's no telling what their effects will be on individuals, society, and even the entire human race.

# CHAPTER 8

# PLAYING WITH YOUR BRAINWAVES

For 75 years, scientists have known that the brain emits certain electrical patterns that can be sensed and categorized. These EEG "waves" come in four varieties, referred to as alpha, beta, theta, and delta. Furthermore, it has long been known that specific brainwaves were associated with specific states of consciousness. For example, when in "alpha," you are generally relaxed; when you are in "beta," you're generally busy doing stuff, or a bit stressed. Yet recently, as the technology of EEG recording has improved, more distinctions have been made so that even peak states of joy, focus, and creativity have been associated with precise brain wave patterns.

In order to make use of this mapping of our brain waves, various products are coming out that aim to tell you what your current brain wave state is, and how you might "nudge" it into something more beneficial. This new field of exploration is generally referred to as "neuro-feedback." Due to the continuing advancement of technology, this once crude attempt at altering our brain waves is gradually becoming better and less expensive.

In 1989 I tried a neuro-feedback device called "The Mind Mirror." It cost several thousand dollars, was the size of a suitcase, and it involved attaching various hard to attach electrodes to your head. Nevertheless, I could see that it had possibilities. Using its constant feedback, I was able to achieve a state of ecstasy in about 30 minutes of training. Later, in 2010, I went to a neuro-feedback therapist to help me deepen my meditation experience. This time the device that was used was more like a video game. I was instructed to make a hot air balloon rise on a computer screen by relaxing my mind. Evidently, as my brain waves moved toward deep meditation, the hot air balloon would rise. It was fun.

Of course, paying thousands or hundreds of dollars for neuro-feedback training is not practical for most people. Therefore, when a product called "The Muse" came out in 2014, I was pretty excited. The Muse is a 4 channel EEG feedback device that you slip on your head in one simple step. Through audio and visual cues that come from your smartphone, you can potentially learn to alter your brain waves toward a more relaxed state of mind. I own a Muse and I have found it to be somewhat helpful, but still a bit cumbersome to use.

The latest in the race for an easy to use and inexpensive neuro-feedback device is something called "The Ifocusband." Although I have not tried the device myself, the reviews from people who have are very intriguing. Virtually all of the many clients who used it during the 2013 PGA tour improved their golf games. The actual device can hide comfortably inside any hat or baseball cap, and according to the folks promoting it, has been proven to improve sports and business performance. To find out more, you can go to www.ifocusband.com.

In due time, many athletes looking for an edge will use various brain training devices such as the Muse or Ifocusband. As the technology gets better and cheaper, such devices may become standard fare for any event in which peak performance is needed. While this may seem a long way off now, consider how quickly smartphones have become an indispensable part of our daily lives. Once a technology hits a tipping point of low cost, extremely useful, and easy to use (think Internet), the world beats a path to its door. Your future may involve wearing a normal looking baseball cap that trains you towards states of peace and ecstasy. If you want, you can get started on that future even today.

**Best Suited** for increasing your Engagement and Pleasure.

**Best Features:** Can be used for any issue; improves with practice; can lead to greater emotional maturity.

**Possible Weaknesses:** It is not easy to use, it's not "invisible" to use, and it costs at least $300.

# CHAPTER 9

# VIABLE VIRTUAL REALITY

For a long time, Virtual Reality (or VR for short) was right around the corner. With the advent of the Oculus Rift headset, it has now arrived. In case you live in a cave, VR is the simulation of the real world with a computer-generated world. The hope and hype surrounding VR is what allowed a 20 year-old kid named Lucky Palmer to sell his little VR headset company (with only a prototype) for two billion dollars to Facebook in 2014. Soon everyone was on the VR bandwagon: Hollywood, TV, makers of porn, the whole shebang.

When a new "medium" comes along, at first no one knows how it will play out. When Thomas Edison invented the phonograph, it never occurred to him it would be used to play music. Thus, Virtual Reality will be tried on everything from VR-type movies to VR-type Skype calls—and eventually we'll see what sticks. But it's safe to say that the line between reality and the "virtual world" will blur, and that will have great implications for how we live and work.

Since this book is about the "technology of joy," it's important to consider how VR might affect our pursuit of happiness. For one thing,

VR will allow people to travel the world virtually. People enjoy traveling, but it can be expensive. Yet, with VR travel, you can take a trip to Antarctica for free, and you don't even have to pack your heavy coat. VR will also make long distance relationships more compelling, especially after good "haptic interfaces" allow folks to feel Virtual Reality hugging, touching, and even sexual activity.

Another aspect of how VR will affect our level of happiness is the fact that VR creates a deep sense of "engagement" (the 'E' in PERMA). Engagement is a word that basically means the ability to get so absorbed in a situation that you lose your normal sense of self. Sometimes it is referred to as "flow," or being "in the zone." Whatever you call it, human beings love it. That's why we like playing sports, going to movies, or getting lost in a hobby. While "engagement" is great fun, it can be hard to achieve in daily life. VR is quite good at creating such lofty states of mind. Of course, we'll figure out a way to abuse such a power, but VR will certainly be used to bring us to "flow states" more frequently.

VR is already being used to help people overcome phobias and Post Traumatic Stress Disorder—or PTSD. In what is called Virtual Reality Therapy, or VRT, patients are exposed to difficult situations in a virtual manner—eventually leading to less anxiety in formerly stressful situations. At a recent conference I went to on "transformational technology," I got to try out a couple of these VRT programs. They were good, and with time they will surely get better.

Yet, it is what we don't know about VR that is likely to have the greatest effects on society. Sure, there will be amazing VR movies and video games, but how about the possibilities of combining VR with other modalities listed in this book. A VR based neuro-feedback mechanism may help us overcome our life long fears in minutes, or train our brainwaves to settle into an ecstatic state of calm in seconds. In addition, VR will surely accelerate our ability to learn new skills. As in the movie *The Matrix*, you may soon be able to learn Kung-Fu in an afternoon.

Perhaps the most controversial aspect of VR is how it will affect our interaction with the real world. Once it's easy to take a virtual Disneyland vacation, or have a virtual relationship, will people still pursue such activities in what some VR folks call "the default world?" If you've seen the movie "Wall-e," or "The Matrix," you know that such a powerful technology is fraught with unanticipated consequences. The guidelines set out in Chapter 45 of this book, "How to Know if a Technology is Your Friend," can be a useful resource. The questions explored in that chapter can help you know what a helpful key to a meaningful life is, and what is just another distraction.

**Best Suited** for increasing your Pleasure and Engagement.

**Best Features**: Ease of use; quick to do; powerful.

**Possible Weaknesses:** It's not "invisible" to use, it may have the "side effect" of being addictive, and initial costs are between $200 and $600.

# CHAPTER 10

# THYNCING YOUR WAY TO PEACE

At the 2015 Consumer Electronic Show in Las Vegas, a gadget named the "Thync" garnered a lot of attention. The Thync is a consumer version of what's known as Transcranial Alternating Current Stimulation, or TACS. TDCS—Transcranial *Direct* Current Stimulation— has been around a long time, and has been shown to have real effects on learning, mental sharpness, and mood. Basically, when you use a Thync, you are placing a curved white gizmo on your forehead that zaps your brain with small amounts of electricity.

When paired via Bluetooth to your smartphone, you can select between a "calm" vibe and an "energy" vibe. The result, if all goes well, is either more mental clarity or an interesting feeling of deep mental relaxation. Each session lasts between 5 and 20 minutes. The feeling of electricity going into your brain can be slightly uncomfortable at first, but with time you tend to get used to it. Since its debut, the folks at Thync have worked hard to come up with new "vibes," including a session that contains a guided meditation, and one that can supposedly help you to go to sleep.

My experiences with the Thync have varied quite a bit. Something is clearly happening, but what happens tends to vary depending on my mood and perhaps other factors. The "calm vibe" has sometimes felt like two stiff drinks, and other times like a nice state of inner peace. To my surprise, the effect seemed to last for a couple of hours after my session was over. When I've used the "energy vibes," I've noticed a bit more mental clarity—but its effects are less noticeable for me than the feelings evoked by the "calm vibes." According to the reviews I've read, most people notice a clear effect, but the effects vary quite a bit from person to person.

In thinking whether or not to get a Thync, you have to consider how satisfied you are with your current ways of feeling mental clarity or deep calm. If you don't have reliable ways to boost your mental clarity or connect with a deep calming sensation, the Thync can be a very helpful tool. Yet, if you're an old hand at meditation, cognitive enhancing substances, and tools to change how you feel, the Thync can feel a bit clunky. It takes some practice to get it to connect in just the right manner, and it can feel a bit uncomfortable at first. Also, if you wear it around the office, you'll have to explain to everyone why you are zapping your brain with electricity.

The Thync costs $299.00. Included in the purchase are 10 "energy strips" and 10 "calm strips". These strips attach to the Thync gadget and are placed at specific locations on your head. You're only supposed to use the strips for single time use, but if you clean your skin before attaching them, you can usually get 2 or 3 uses out of each of them. This is important since replacement strips are expensive. Five replacement strips cost $20, so if you use your Thync a lot, it'll run you about the cost of a cup of coffee each time.

In Chapter 44, I talk about "mixing and matching" various modalities from this book. If you're somewhat of a budding mad scientist (like me), you can use the Thync to see what effect it has in combination with other tools, pills, and gadgets. I have found that combining the Thync with meditation type audio's (Chapter 14) or cognitive enhancers (Chapter 2) has a way of "turbo charging" those modalities. Of course, the folks at Thync don't recommend such experimentation, but I haven't found there to be any negative side effects from such practices. You may get lucky and find a combination that truly rocks your world.

Thync has only been out a few months. The company has energetically pursued feedback as to what seems to work well for people, and what does not. They have also consistently improved their app, and are evidently researching ever new "waveforms" people can use to feel better. It is my guess that the technology and how to use it will gradually improve over time. Such technologies tend to start off a bit clunky, but with steady improvement can turn into a "must have" item—think iPod—before you know it.

**Best Suited** for increasing Pleasure and Engagement.

**Best Features:** Can be used for any issue; can affect the body, mind, and emotions.

**Possible Weaknesses**: Cost, takes a while to set up, and it's not "invisible."

# CHAPTER 11

# AN EAR CLIP TO UNLOCK YOUR HEART

About twenty years ago, I visited a small community known as the Institute of Heartmath near Boulder Creek, California. At the time, they were a rag-tag group of aging hippies, spiritual seekers, and scientists with a mission to demonstrate the power of the heart to change the world. Flash forward 20 years, and they are now a major organization whose clients include Fortune 100 companies, the U.S. Army, Air Force, hospitals, and tens of thousands of people. Along the way, they have developed various products for training people to reach what they call a state of "coherence."

According to their website, "Coherence is a state of internal synchronization between the heart, breath, and the head. People experience coherence as a sense of inner calm and balance, and increased focus." To help people reach a state of coherence easily, Heartmath has created three major products: the Inner Balance app (only for IPhones and IPads), the Emwave2 handheld device (no smartphone needed), and the Emwave Pro (for use with your computer.) All these products use similar technology to track and teach you to move away from stress and towards greater coherence.

I've used all three of these products, and after a bit of training, they are each very easy to use and quite effective. It's gratifying to see your ability to reach a state of coherence increase with each session. The Emwave Pro and Emwave 2 even have games you can "play" to increase your ability to quickly enter a heart-centered state of mind and body. With practice, in as little as a couple of minutes, the real time visual and auditory feedback you receive helps you to enter into a rather peaceful, loving, and alert state of mind.

The Heartmath technologies are all based on measuring something called Heart Rate Variability, or HRV for short. All their products use a small sensor that clips onto your earlobe—or on your finger to help measure your HRV. In brief, HRV is a measurement of the timing between each heart-beat. Basically, the more consistent the timing between your heart beats, the higher your coherence score. A wide range of benefits result from sustaining a highly coherent state—even for short periods. Numerous independent research studies have validated benefits such as:

1. Better control of your emotional reactions.
2. 40% improvement in long-term memory and 24% improvement in short-term memory.
3. Increased ability to focus and concentrate.
4. Reduced anxiety, stress, and fatigue, and increased productivity and sleep quality.

The scientific findings the Heartmath Institute have collected are impressive. Yet for me, perhaps the greatest benefit is that "high coherence" feels—dare I say it—joyful. It feels really good to be in a state of relaxed and alert balance. It's not quite a state of meditative relaxation. Instead, I would describe it as a state of heart centered focus and alertness. It just feels balanced and "right." From this state of mind and body, it's easy to feel compassionate or ready to make good decisions. Once you're in a state of high coherence, you wonder why you got so stressed out and left that experience in the first place.

Along with the Heartmath products, their websites www.heartmath.com and www.heartmath.org offer many books, videos, audio's, and background information that can be useful. One of their most powerful and useful methods is known as the "Quick Coherence" technique. Basically, this method consists of three simple steps:

1. Focus your attention on the center of your chest. At first, it can help to place a hand at this spot to help you focus your attention there.
2. Breathe slowly and deeply into the center of your chest. As you inhale, feel as if your breath is flowing in through the heart, and as you exhale, feel it leaving this area.
3. Finally, activate a "heart feeling." While continuing to feel as if you are breathing through your heart, do whatever helps you to activate a positive feeling. This can involve remembering special places or times with a beloved child, person, or pet. The goal is to feel a positive feeling such as gratitude, love, appreciation, honor, care, or compassion.

I teach the Quick Coherence technique in many of my seminars, and people love it. In as little as 60 seconds, you can go from stressed-out to joyed out, or if you prefer—from pissed to joy. With practice, I've found I can "amp up" my heart feeling even more by focusing on the love I have for my wife—or even better—my dog! I simply remember special times with my Golden Retriever, such as her rollicking happily through a field of grass. Then, (in my mind) I call her by one of my nicknames for her, such as, "My little smoocher poocher." (Those who love a dog will understand this method more than those who don't!). Anyway, such a remembrance never fails to open my heart and calm my mind.

Although the Heartmath products are helpful for increasing your level of heart coherence, you can practice the Quick Coherence technique simply on your own without their gadgets. However, I must admit that there is something about getting real time feedback that helps you to stay with a technique and gradually get better at it.

Recently I talked to the helpful support staff at Heartmath, and they suggested a person start with five minute sessions on their products, and practice three or four times a day. Each of their products allow you to increase the level of difficulty until you can achieve a high state of coherence rather quickly and easily. Heartmath's HRV measuring products start at $129, and go up from there. I have found their techniques and products to be one of the easiest and best ways to recover from stress and reach a really good state of mind and body. If you're looking for a high tech gadget for recovering from stress, their products can be a smart place to start.

**Best Suited** for increasing Pleasure, Engagement, and Accomplishment.

**Best Features:** For any issue, improves with practice, affects body, mind and emotions, and can lead to emotional maturity.

**Possible Weaknesses**: Cost, is not "invisible," and takes some time to learn.

# CHAPTER 12

# BODY GADGETS TO OPEN YOU UP

If you're like me, you've accumulated a few bad habits over the years. Perhaps you have a tendency to slouch while working on your laptop, or you forget to breathe deeply, or you fail to take short breaks when you're feeling tense. Well, you no longer need despair. High tech hope is now available. If you tend to slouch or display bad posture, the Lumo Lift can save the day. If you forget to take stress breaks, or fail to breathe deeply throughout your day, the Spire can become your new automated friend.

Of course, there are new fitness wearables that seem to be coming out daily. If you want to know how many steps you take a day, or how much you exercised this week compared to last week, you have dozens of products to choose from. Yet, that was not my interest. I already exercise each week, and wearing a bracelet around my wrist was not going to change that. What I needed was something simple that could help me break some long standing bad habits—such as slouching when at my desk or forgetting to breathe deeply when stressed. Today, we have the technology to attend to both these problems.

The Lumo Lift (about $80, or two for $99) is a device you wear below your collar-bone to help remind you to sit up straight. You put its half inch square magnet on the outside of your shirt, and this magnet holds its one inch long plastic gizmo on the inside of your shirt (or blouse). Then, according to its website, "The Lumo Lift tracks your posture and activity. Using subtle vibrations as feedback, it will gently vibrate to remind you to straighten up your posture every time you begin to slouch. Patented biomechanics monitoring sensors in the Lumo Lift use angle displacement as a measure to let you know when your body slouches away from what you've calibrated as your standard of good posture."

My experience with the Lumo Lift has been mixed. I like the idea, but sometimes it vibrates when I seem to be sitting up straight. Perhaps I'm doing something wrong, but if I am, then other people will probably make a similar mistake. As with all new technologies, it will likely get better over time. Yet, since posture affects both how our body feels and our mood, the idea of a "vibrating postural coach" strikes me as a smart move.

Along with having good posture, nothing is more important than deep and regular breathing if you want to feel good and stay relaxed. In order to help remind yourself of this important activity, the Spire was invented. In the words of its website, "Spire measures your breathing patterns to give you insights into your state of mind. It can notify you when your breathing reflects tension and guide you to calm or remind you to be more active when you're sedentary. Spire also helps you discover what makes you calm, focused, and active, and coaches you to a more mindful and healthy lifestyle."

The Spire (about $150) is a 1.5 inch long gizmo that clips onto your belt, waist band, or even your bra. It monitors your breathing pattern, and can even show you in real time (on the accompanying app) how well you're breathing. The reviews on Amazon for the Spire are quite enthusiastic. Here is a typical one: "Spire is so tuned into me and my body, it even lets me know if I'm tense and could use a quick 2 minute meditation boost. The first time I tried a boost, I was stressed and my mind kept telling me it wasn't going to work, it wasn't going to work- yet at the end of the boost, I actually found myself laughing with happiness! I realized it not only worked but I was so much calmer. Spire is amazing. It's like a personal buddy at your side, helping you be your best each day."

That being said, I have found I have the same problem with Spire as I do with the Lumo Lift. It sometimes vibrates when I'm not stressed, or fails to vibrate when I am stressed. Also, both the Spire and the Lumo Lift require their apps be opened and active while you use them—and this takes a certain amount of battery life. In addition, if you try to use both together, it can definitely be confusing. Yet, having gentle reminders to de-stress—even if not always "accurate," is better than nothing. I expect that as their bugs get worked out, the Spire and Lumo Lift will be both easier to use and more accurate.

Personally, I'm looking forward to the day when one device accurately tracks my breathing, posture, and even my feelings. Till that day arrives, if you want an occasional nudge (or vibration) to remind you to sit up and breathe deeply, the Spire and Lumo Lift can fit the bill.

**Best Suited** for increasing Pleasure and Engagement.

**Best Features:** Can be done anywhere, it is invisible, can affect the body, mind, and emotions, and they can improve with practice.

**Possible Weaknesses:** Can be a bit tricky to use, and they have an initial cost.

# CHAPTER 13

# THE VARIETY OF VIDEO GAMES

You may think you know video games. After all, this 74 billion dollar a year industry is even bigger than the movie or music industry. But until recently, this relatively new form of entertainment was dominated by violent shoot 'em ups. According to many researchers, killing people on video screens is better suited for increasing aggression than for creating joy and happiness. Yet, in the world of technology, things are always changing. Nowadays, if playing in violent, action packed worlds does not float your boat, you have plenty of other choices that might just bring you what you're looking for.

Brad Bushman, a professor at Ohio State University states, "With all the evidence about the dangers of violent video games, it's good to know that game players can choose games that will provide a positive experience. Relaxing video games put people in a good mood. And when people are in a good mood, they are more inclined to help others, and that's better for everyone." Dr. Bushman goes on to note that relaxing video games are rated by college students as being just as entertaining and enjoyable as neutral or violent video games.

In fact, Daniel Johnson of the QUT games research lab has shown that, with clinically depressed adults, there are many positive outcomes from playing video games. Mr. Johnson found certain video games have been shown to reduce tension, anger, depression and fatigue. Research focusing on video game play among children has suggested that the best outcomes are associated with moderate video game play, as opposed to no play or excessive play. These benefits have extended to greater positive emotions, having less risky friendship networks, better self-esteem and higher levels of family closeness.

Of course, one person's violent video game is another person's way of relaxing and having fun. Therefore, when exploring video games, you have to try a bunch and see what works for you. Yet, it can be helpful to know that there are a wide variety of video genres, and they each keep getting better over time. Besides the obvious action packed and violent genre, there are genres dedicated to relaxing games, puzzles, simulations, learning, gaining certain skills, and even becoming more motivated at work.

In order to give you a quick overview of some of the best that's out there, I'll mention some of the video games that are most popular or most conducive to a life of joy. For those who like intense action, of course there are the long time bestsellers like Grand Theft Auto, Call of Duty, Halo, Mortal Kombat, and Minecraft. For those who like some good, simple, fun games, Candy Crush, Farmville, and Angry Birds are popular.

Any game that can get you dancing, moving, or enjoying music more is likely to make you happy. An additional advantage to these games is the fact that they can often be shared with your friends and family. Popular titles along these lines include "Just Dance" and "Dance Central." When it comes to music video games, the "Guitar Hero" series and its various rock band offshoots can be clean, good fun.

Next there is the category of sports games. With the advent of body motion detectors, many video games are now becoming increasingly like the real thing. Whether you like tennis, golf, or bowling, you can now do a reasonable facsimile of these sports in the comfort of your living room. Many parents especially like connecting with their kids while playing a video style sport game.

Not only are there thousands of video games, there are also many different "platforms" to play them on. With the popularity of smartphones, most video games now have a mobile version that they can be played on. Yet, if you want to have your video seem more immersive, you'll need some kind of video console. Popular ones include the Xbox, Nintendo, Wii, and Play Station. They each have their advantages which you can best learn about online or at an electronics store. Fortunately, a lot of the best games are available on any platform that you may have purchased.

In her important book, *Reality is Broken: Why Games Make Us Better and How They Can Change the World*, Jane McGonigal writes about how games can be a force for good. She states, "Games make us happy because they are hard work that we choose for ourselves, and it turns out that almost nothing makes us happier than good hard work." Ms. McGonigal describes in her book how video games can be used for everything from fixing real-world social problems like depression, to helping global issues like climate change.

Before I overwhelm you with even more options and information, let me just state that if you're looking for a certain type of video game, just Google it. For example, you might try Googling something like "Top 10 relaxing video games," or "Top 10 video games that make you happy." Recently when I did that, the games "LocoRoco," "Animal Crossing," "Endless Ocean," and "Flow," came up. Yet, in this ever changing field, by the time you read this you'll likely have a whole new list to choose from.

As with any highly entertaining experience, one must be careful to avoid addiction when entering the world of video games. In a medium in which 25% of "gamers" are over the age of 50, video game addiction is not just a problem for teens. Ultimately, in an age of endless choice, it's up to you to decide what to allow into your brain—and when it's time to stop playing a game.

**Best Suited** for increasing Pleasure and Engagement, and Accomplishment.

**Best Features:** Quick and powerful effect.

**Possible Shortcomings:** Can be addictive, not "invisible," and can't be done anywhere.

# CHAPTER 14

# SOUNDS THAT MEDITATE YOU

I first came upon audio CDs that proclaimed to quickly "induce states of ecstasy like you're a Zen monk," in the 1980's. They had good advertising copy, but poor results. Various companies declared that their CDs could do everything from help you to astral project, to help you make millions of dollars. I was a bit of a sucker—so I tried a lot of them. Eventually, I grew cynical and gave up on the field.

Then, something interesting happened. These "high tech sounds" gradually got better and their advertising copy got more humble. In 2012, a friend of mine suggested I try Holosync CDs. I belittled such technology, saying "such things did nothing for me." But my friend persisted, and soon I tried a CD. It was clear that the binaural beats of this CD were playing with my brainwaves—big time. In fact, they had scientific evidence that the various sounds on their CDs could affect brainwave patterns by a process known as "brain wave entrainment."

In its simplest terms, brain wave entrainment is the tendency for your brain waves to align or "entrain" with their environment. Our brain is always reorganizing itself and forming new EEG patterns and neural connections. By supplying your ears with specific sound patterns at different frequencies and rhythms, your brain waves are, in turn, affected. In modern day life, people spend a lot of their lives in the "beta" brain wave state. Yet, through listening to these high tech sound environments, people can be guided to experience more "alpha," "theta", or even "delta" brain wave patterns.

Traditionally, "alpha" is the brain wave pattern associated with deep relaxation. "Theta" is often associated with creativity, and "Delta" with deep sleep or deep meditation. Each of the programs described here have audio sessions geared towards taking a person from their normal (often Beta) brain wave pattern, towards the three other brain wave patterns. Some of the sessions simply sound like rain, or the ocean, while others can sound like monks chanting "om," or have various repetitive musical patterns.

Holosync CDs (and now downloads) are still the number one seller in the field, though they have plenty of competition. Word on the street from the people I've talked to is that Holosync is pretty industrial strength. It has literally dozens of levels, and as you progress through them, it can "bring up" a lot of past psychological stuff, and greatly impact your life and brain. That can be good if you want to make conscious your "stuff," and bad if you simply want an easy way to feel good. Of course, people react differently to these types of things, so your results may vary. You can learn more about Holosync at its website, centerpointe.com.

A direct competitor to Holosync is a company called Life Flow (project-meditation.com). Life Flow is a lot less expensive than Holosync, but also has less customer support. In addition, most people say Life Flow is not as impactful as Holosync, but if you'd like to avoid having a lot of old issues come up for you, that can be a good thing. As with Holosync, many people report deep relaxation, unusual dreams, and eventually a deeper clarity of mind.

Another major player in the field of "high tech sounds," is the company known as Iawake. You can find them at www.iawaketechnologies.com. Iawake has literally dozens of products, ranging from binaural beats behind rainfall type sounds, to complex, multilevel musical compositions that play with your brain and bio field. If you go to their website, you can download some free samples and get descriptions of what each product is geared towards. Some of their products are (like Holosync and Life Flow) meant to be used only with headphones. Yet, they also have products that can be used as background sounds over speakers.

I find that I mostly listen to Iawake stuff—partly because I like the variety they offer. They have programs ranging from leading you into profound states of meditation to programs for a quick energy burst. By reading the descriptions of their programs and some trial and error, you can probably find something that works pretty well for you. As with all programs of self-improvement, you tend to get out of them what you put into them. If you listen occasionally to simply get relaxed, you can certainly get that. However, if you consistently invest an hour a day to their use, you'll likely experience an inner journey through various levels of your mind and psychology.

Many of the companies that sell these audio's purport they can be an easy substitute for meditation. Since I am a long time meditator, I can tell you they can definitely induce meditation like experiences. In fact, studies show that both long-term meditators and consistent users of these type of audio's can increase the amount of alpha, theta, and delta waves they regularly experience. Yet, I find that I can't go as deep with these audio's as I do when I meditate—but then again, I've been meditating every day for 40 years. I know of many people who have found doing daily meditation to be difficult, but have enjoyed and benefitted from binaural beat type audios. Ultimately, you just have to experiment and see if these high tech sound environments “work” for you.

**Best Suited** for increasing your Pleasure and Engagement.

**Best Features:** Easy to use, improves with practice, and can affect the body, mind, and emotions.

**Possible Shortcomings:** Cost, can have temporary negative side effects, and is visible to others.

# CHAPTER 15

# LETTING YOUR INNER ROCK STAR OUT

One of the quickest and most reliable ways to feel more joy in your life is to sing. For thousands of years, people have sung and played music in order to feel the full range of human feelings. However, with the advent of karaoke, people have been given the power to easily sing along to their favorite tunes—and let their inner rock star out. Whereas karaoke "systems" used to cost thousands of dollars, nowadays you can buy an adequate karaoke machine for about $100. If you have a bit more to spend on your "investment of joy," you can even buy a machine that *makes* you sound like a true singing professional.

I have a mediocre voice at best. My friends tell me that, on my good days, I sound like Bob Dylan. I *don't* take that as a complement. Yet, about a year ago I bought a machine called a "Singtrix" (you can learn more at www.singtrix.com). The Singtrix includes a microphone, a 40 watt speaker/amplifier, and most importantly, a versatile voice synthesizing unit. Basically, you sing into the microphone, and the Singtrix makes your voice sound *awesome*. You can choose between 300 different voice altering sounds, but for me, I appreciate that it automatically corrects your pitch—so you sound on *key*—even when you're not.

There's something magical to singing into a microphone and having your voice come out sounding like a five-part harmony choir—or Elvis Presley. I love watching people try it for the first time. It's as if we've always wanted to sound like Adele or Frank Sinatra, but we didn't even realize it. Now that the Singtrix makes that possible, you can experience much of the joy of being a rock star—without having to spend the rest of your life taking voice lessons and living on the road. Just last night several friends of mine came over and we sang, laughed, cheered, and applauded our way into a state of total ecstasy. It's a lot of clean, good fun, and at $245 (at Amazon), the price is reasonable.

If you're short on money, but you still want to experience the joys of karaoke, you can pick up a Memorex MKS-SS2 Sing Stand2 for about $70. This unit includes a microphone, a speaker, and an ability to connect with an MP3 player. I'd like to tell you that you can have as much joy with this unit as with the Singtrix. Yet, in actuality, there's a big difference. But don't let the pursuit of perfection get in the way of a good and low cost time. Singing is just plain fun. Now that there are karaoke versions of thousands of popular songs on Youtube.com, you don't need a fancy unit to enjoy singing with your favorite tunes. Just plug in your microphone and go to Youtube.com. Then, type in the name of a favorite song, followed by the word "karaoke." You'll see a number of entries pop up. Choose one that seems popular and start wailing away.

If you're looking for a low cost karaoke machine that is versatile and comes complete with everything, you can do no wrong with the "Karaoke USA" machine. This fine little unit has internal speakers, accepts karaoke CD's and DVD's, and it allows for MP3's and has a USB connection. Furthermore, it comes with two microphones, it can record your voice, and it even includes its own screen for singing with the lyrics. That's a lot of value for a mere $130. If you're looking for a unit that is both complete and flexible, this would be a good place to start.

Rather than bore you with reviewing more machines, let me implore you to not miss out on the joy of singing. Singing is one of the best ways to tap into powerful positive feelings. It's almost impossible to sing a song like "Twist and Shout" by the Beatles and *not* feel fantastic. Unfortunately, many adults are hesitant to sing because they feel their voice doesn't sound good enough. To them I say, "Get over it!" My voice sounds like crap, but I don't let that stop me. Besides, people care more about your level of enthusiasm than whether or not you are perfectly on pitch. However, if you're a perfectionist and simply can't "get over it," then get a Singtrix unit. You'll sound almost as good as Adele, but you won't have the burden of being mobbed once you step outside your house.

**Best Suited** for increasing Pleasure, Engagement, and Relationships.

**Best Features:** Powerful effect, no negative effects, and it improves with practice.

**Possible Shortcomings**: Can't be done in most places, cost, and takes some time to set up.

SECTION THREE

# PSYCHOLOGICAL TECHNIQUES

"I don't care what your chat group says. I say you're becoming overly dependent on technological gadgetry."

Ever since the 1960's, people have created a plethora of psychological methods to help folks "get high." A lot of these methods never made it out of the 60's, due to their ineffectiveness or the fact that the times have changed. Although dancing naked in a group while listening to Jimi Hendrix can still get you high, such behavior is no longer considered "acceptable." However, some psychologically based methods have withstood the test of time—and/or have been scientifically verified to be truly effective. In this section, I'll go over some of my favorites. While you may have tried or heard of some of these techniques, many will be new to you. New is good. You never know when you'll discover a method that just "clicks" with you—and could propel you to new heights of joy and ecstasy...

# CHAPTER 16

# DEEP WISDOM OF THE TALKING STICK

In one form or another, the "Talking Stick" has been used for thousands of years. Having traveled to some remote villages in Africa, I've even seen men and women who still sit around the campfire each night and use this ancient—but still magical—method. In essence, the Talking Stick allows one person of a group to say whatever they feel compelled or called to say, while the other people in the group listen attentively without interruption or comment. That's the basic method. However, the mechanics of this method can't begin to explain the miraculous things that can result from its use.

For many years, I was part of a spiritual group that used a Talking Stick "set up." Every Sunday, our group of friends would gather at a specific time and location and sit silently for about 15 minutes while music played. Although the music differed each week, it was always music aimed at putting us in our hearts, or helping us feel the depth of our lives. After the music played, one of the leaders of the group would sit in a chair in front of the rest of the folks and begin speaking what was in their hearts. In our case, the "stick" was actually a special chair, but the effect was the same.

I was always amazed at how well this set up consistently worked. No matter who sat in the chair and talked, it seemed it always helped reveal that person's deeper essence, wisdom, and heartfelt perspective in life. Even people whom I didn't like or respect would suddenly seem transformed by this simple method. Sure, sometimes I would be bored, but most of the time I would be inspired or even be moved to tears. Once the first person was done talking, he or she would ask if anyone else felt inspired to talk. The person who had just talked would choose one of the folks with their hand raised, and the next Talking Stick adventure would begin. Typically, people would talk for 15 to 30 minutes, but there were no hard and fast rules.

Occasionally, I would be the person chosen to speak in the "Talking Chair." When that would happen, I would invariably be nervous because I had no idea what I was going to say. Yet, sitting in that chair, looking out at all the sincere faces listening attentively, somehow something magical would be evoked in me. I would simply try to be honest, say what I'm learning or seeing in life, and voila, heartfelt poetry would pour out of my mouth. It was fun to listen to what I had to say! Often, I was as surprised as those who were listening to me…

If you are going to explore this method, I have a few suggestions for you. First, although it can be done with just two people (one speaker and one listener), I find it generally works better when more than two people are participating. Second, it's important to create a sacred space before a person begins talking. This can be done through listening to music, meditating, creating some shared ritual, or even simply being quiet for a period of time. Third it's helpful to have a leader who can begin the meeting, choose follow-up speakers, and announce the end of the session. Having such a person who can provide some structure is useful in creating a relaxed "container" for the magic of this method to occur in.

If you've never seen or done this method, I think you'll be pleasantly surprised. The Quaker religion adopted a version of the Talking Stick (which they call *Waiting Worship)* that they use in many of their services. Of course, you don't need a special stick or chair to signify who is the speaker, but creating a special stick or chair seems helpful for setting up this sacred ritual. In a world of non-stop noise, competition, and distractions, the Talking Stick can be a soothing balm to help people go below the surface and find the wisdom within.

**Best Suited** for increasing Meaning, Engagement, and Relationships.

**Best Features**: Powerful effect, no cost, improves with practice, and can lead to spiritual maturity.

**Possible Shortcomings:** Takes some work to set up properly, and takes a while to actually do.

# CHAPTER 17

# THE FULL RELEASE METHOD OF LETTING GO

Perhaps the most important thing a human being can learn is how to quickly let go of negative thought patterns and emotions. By doing that, you can learn to quickly return to the peace and love hidden behind our turbulent minds. Once you can do this effectively and efficiently, everything in your life changes. For several years I've studied various methods for quickly letting go of negative emotions. Two of my favorite techniques derive from the same enlightened teacher—a man named Lester Levenson.

Lester had an interesting story. After being told he had less than two weeks left to live after a massive second heart attack, Lester went home to die. In preparation for dying, he came upon a simple way to let go of negative emotions. Well, as he let go of negative thoughts and emotions, his health improved. Within a few months, he was perpetually free of negative emotions and continuously in touch with complete peace of mind. Lester went on to live 43 more years, and founded both the Sedona Method and Release Technique.

In my use of these methods, I found both of them to be very similar and very effective. In order to make them even more effective, I altered them in some ways so they would work better for me and for the people I was helping. If you want to know about either of the techniques that Lester spearheaded, you can find out more information at www.Sedona.com or www.releasetechnique.com. I can heartily recommend their books and courses.

While my brief description of these methods is somewhat simplified, sometimes the simplest tools are the most effective. For those of you who are already familiar with the Sedona Method or the Release Technique, you'll notice that I have added the repeated prompting of physical ways to release negative emotions. I have found this to be an effective aid to truly letting go of negative emotions easily and effectively.

In order to use this method on yourself, consider recording the following words into your smartphone. That way, you can easily be guided to release anytime you have an issue that you'd like to let go of. I have found that, when "overtaken" by negative emotions, it can be hard to use *any* method. By having this recording on your phone, all you need do is hit "play," and you'll be guided to let go of whatever story you are stuck in. Nothing could be easier.

Once you're in a comfortable place where you won't be interrupted, listen to your recording of the following words read very slowly. The words in parentheses are not meant to be read into your smartphone. They are simply to help explain what I've written and/or to help you with the pacing of your speech.

Read these words into your smartphone:

**Allow yourself to notice or remember any uncomfortable situation that has left you feeling stressed in any way. Normally, we resist or distract ourselves from our negative emotions. Instead, welcome**

whatever your current experience is. (Pause for about 10 seconds). Take time to welcome or appreciate your bodily feelings, like you would *welcome* or appreciate an old friend. (Pause for a few seconds) Become curious as to where and how such thoughts or feelings actually *feel* in your body right at this moment. (Pause).

If you notice you're still resisting your experience, welcome the resistance—the way you would a small child—with open arms and a smile. (Pause). Allow your current experience to be there—exactly as it is. (Pause).

Once you've fully welcomed or allowed your experience to be as it is, ask yourself, "Has this uncomfortable feeling resulted from my wanting Control, or Approval, or Safety, or my wanting to feel more Separate—such as wanting to be right or put others down?" (Pause). Take note of which desire feels the strongest in you.

Once you're clear on what desire—control, approval, safety, or separation—you have *most* wanted in this situation, ask yourself, "*Could* I let go of grasping after *that* desire (control, approval, safety/ security, or separation) just for the next 20 seconds?" (Pause). Realize it is your feeling of "wanting" or lack that creates your suffering, and resolve to let that feeling of lack go. (Pause).

Take a deep breath and allow yourself to let go of craving or needing whatever you felt you were needing—just for now. It may help to yawn, shake, let your jaw hang loose, or make loud sighing sounds as you attempt to let go of being constricted in your body and emotions. (Pause).

Now ask yourself, "Could I let go some more? (pause) Could I realize these feelings are just the result of a story I got running in my head? Could I choose to let go of my story just for right now and feel the stillness underneath?" (Pause) Now feel where you felt the

**uncomfortable emotions—such as in your chest or stomach area—and imagine opening up a window there and letting the energy and feeling pass through you—dispersing into the air or down into the Earth. Once again take a deep breath and either yawn, shake, sigh, or whatever feels right to do to let go of the stuck energy in your body. (Pause) With each breath you exhale, allow the feelings to disperse even more. Feel the spaciousness inside of you. (Pause).**

**Ask yourself, "Could I let go of trying to figure out how to handle this situation, and instead surrender this problem to Beingness? Could I realize I don't know how this whole thing turns out, and that it's better to just let go trying to figure it all out—and instead trust that things will work out in the end?" (Pause).**

**Now think of a person, an animal, or a young child you have great affection for, and remember a time when you felt especially close to them. (Pause). Think of how grateful you are to have this being in your life. (Pause). If it helps, imagine hugging or holding this being, and allow yourself to feel even *more* connected in your heart to them. Enjoy the feelings of heartfelt connection. (Pause). Now think of what you appreciate about *you,* whether it be something you're proud of, or just some trait you have that you're grateful you have, or simply send yourself some compassion and approval. You deserve it. (Pause). Allow yourself to feel appreciation for yourself and all that you do. (Pause) Take your time, but when you're ready, slowly come back to the room. (Pause). Then, when you're ready, begin to open your eyes.**

The more you practice this form of "letting go," the more you'll become free of negative feelings and the more you'll be able to tune into the peace and love that's always inside of you. At first, this may take 5 to 7 minutes to do, but you can eventually learn to let go of small upsets in under a minute.

I started doing The Sedona Method several years ago. At first, I thought of it as just another self-help method. Yet, as I practiced it and looked at how versatile it was, it became one of my favorite techniques of all time. Knowing I could easily let go of unwanted feelings helped me to feel safe to truly *feel* my feelings—rather than distract myself from them. That made a huge difference in my life. After using it for a while, I realized that adding physical helpers to release (such as yawning, shaking, sighing, etc.) made it even *more* effective. In addition, what I now call the "Full Release Method" actually satisfies ALL of the 14 criteria for a really useful and wide-ranging method. No other method I know of manages to do that—so it's worth a try!

**Best Suited** for increasing Pleasure, Engagement, Relationships, and Meaning.

**Best Features**: Easy, for any issue, no cost, can be done anywhere, can be done on root issues, can lead to greater maturity, and improves with practice.

**Possible Shortcomings**: It takes several minutes at first, and may not be very powerful until it is used a few times.

# CHAPTER 18

# THREE GOOD THINGS FOR HAPPINESS

In the last two decades, there have been a lot of studies to test which (if any) methods can dramatically increase one's level of happiness in a short period of time. The good news is that many methods have been repeatedly shown to be amazingly effective. One of the most effective ever studied is called *Three Good Things*.

Positive Psychology pioneer Dr. Marty Seligman created the method I will outline here. This technique is *so* powerful that doing it for only one week has been shown to increase your level of happiness by up to 25% six *months* later. Now I don't know if that sounds like much to you, but in the world of happiness research, this scientifically validated outcome blew everyone away. In fact, if your income were suddenly doubled tomorrow, your happiness level would only go up 25% on average. Then, within six months it would drop down to where it is now. Yet, with the Three Good Things method, your 25% increase actually maintains and does not drop back down. Amazing.

The Three Good Things method Dr. Seligman came up with has three simple parts. The first part is to think of something that happened to you during your day that you felt was good, or in some way made you happy. It can be a little thing such as your appreciation of the day's weather, a nice conversation, or even the yummy sandwich you had for lunch. Step two is to simply write down in a journal or on a piece of paper what it *was* that made you feel good. Step three, which Dr. Seligman emphasizes is the most important part of this exercise, is to reflect on *your* role in creating that moment of goodness or happiness. That's it.

Doing these three steps should really take less than a minute or so to complete. Then you repeat this exercise two more times so you have a total of three good things you've written down, each time asking yourself, "*Why* did that good thing happen to me today?"

In order to make this exercise a bit more clear, I'll use an example of me coaching a workshop participant through this process. After explaining the process to the audience, I asked for a volunteer to work with. A woman named Sharon raised her hand, and I asked her to come up with the first good thing that had happened to her that day. She said, "Well I've liked this workshop so far. That's good." I said, "Great. Not only have you come up with a good thing, but it also shows you're a woman of discriminating taste."

Now if she were doing this exercise on her own, step two would involve her writing this down. Of course, instead of writing this stuff down, you can always do it *verbally* with your mate or a friend. Anyway, back to my workshop. Next, I asked Sharon *why* did this good thing happen—this going to the workshop and enjoying herself. She thought for a moment and then tentatively replied, "I guess it happened because I signed up for it." I explained to Sharon that, though her answer was technically correct, it didn't point to something *specific* about *her* or her *character* that she could feel good about. So I asked her straightaway, "What about *you* made it so you'd sign up for a personal growth workshop?"

She replied, "I guess I'm desperate." Her answer wasn't really what I had in mind, but sometimes you've got to roll with the punches.

So I said to her, "That may be true, but there's also a *positive* reason why you signed up. After all, there are a lot of desperate people in the world, but not all of them sign up for one of my workshops. Yet, *you* did. Despite feeling down, you invested your hard earned dollars in hopes you could learn something that would change your life. That means you still have hope, you still have curiosity, and you're still willing to learn. *That's* why you signed up for this workshop; and not only did you sign up for the workshop, but you're finding *value* in it. Not everybody does. Some people go to a workshop like this and their cynicism or something else blocks them from enjoying it. But you, on the other hand, are *still* open to learning. You may think this is a good workshop, but in reality it's *your* openness to learning that's creating your good experience."

After I said all this, a tear slowly dripped down Sharon's face. I asked her, "What's going on?" She replied, "I sometimes get down on myself, thinking I'm hopeless. But now I see that there's plenty of reason to have hope. There's some goodness in me."

Hopefully, you can get a glimpse of the power of this method. Yet, having watched how lazy I can be, as well as the laziness manifested by other people, I feel I need to let you know of an even easier way to do this exercise. While it's best to come up with three good things per day to list—and then ask why each thing happened, if you're as lazy as I am, you may choose to only list one or two good things per day. It's *still* effective, and instead of taking 2 to 3 minutes to do each night, it only takes one or two minutes to do.

I've given this method out to a lot of people. I've seen its power. When you really get that certain traits or things about you help create positive moments in your life, your life changes. You begin to look at the world through new lenses. You start to understand that no matter how difficult a situation you're in, your ability to laugh, or connect with others, or whatever is good about *you* can help create a special moment. The power *is* within you.

Whatever you feel, allow yourself to *savor* that good feeling for a few moments. Don't short change yourself by rushing off to the next "good thing" before really *feeling* your pride or gratitude for helping to create a good moment. Such feelings are like a healthy tonic that help to feed hope and happiness within you. At first, this exercise may not feel transformational, but as you do it each day, its effect gradually increases. Before you know it, you'll realize that you've become a significantly happier person.

**Best Suited** for increasing Pleasure, Engagement, Relationships, Meaning, and Accomplishment. (The only method I've encountered that hits all five PERMA ingredients!)

**Best Features**: Easy to use, improves with practice, can lead to spiritual maturity, can help others, no cost, not visible to others, can be done anywhere, and no negative side effects.

**Possible Shortcomings:** Doesn't attend to underlying psychological issues, requires a bit of discipline to do each day, and it takes a while for its full power to be felt.

# CHAPTER 19

# THE NUMBER ONE HAPPINESS BOOSTER

In 1994, I got to interview the Dalai Lama for a book I was doing called *The Experience of God*. During our interview, he said something that has stayed with me till this day. When I asked him, "How do you tune into the sacred during your daily life?" His answer was, "Through kindness. Kindness is my religion." Later, when I was doing research for a book called *Find Happiness Now*, I learned an important fact about kindness. According to research, the number one proven way to boost your *own* happiness level is to perform an act of kindness for a stranger or a friend. Kindness is clearly a powerful tool.

Everyone knows it's good to be kind, so why is it so rare in today's world? First, we haven't made a clear connection between our doing acts of kindness and our level of happiness. Our culture, through movies, advertising, and songs, helps us make the connection between having money and being happy. Yet, we don't see endless advertisements associating acts of kindness with joy. Instead, many of us think of acts of kindness as being a sacrifice—or an attempt to be a good person. But if we really knew that kindness was the #1 happiness booster, we might do it more often just because we enjoy it.

Another reason I think we haven't really unleashed the power of kindness is we haven't come up with a specific method for tapping into it. In order to fully appreciate the benefits of kindness, I believe it's important to turn it into a precise method. The second time I was on the Oprah show, she and I had a nice exchange about a method for tapping into kindness using a specific "method." I have transcribed that interaction with her for you to read below:

**Me**: Kindness is one of the quickest ways to make your relationships, your job, everything be more enjoyable. And kindness is free, it has no calories, it's not fattening, and it feels great.

**Oprah:** Right, so you're recommending—and I think everybody should try this, just try this okay—doing a one-week kindness experiment...

**Me:** Yes, that's the way to really get a sense of this. If you do two nice things for people around you every day for a week, you get hooked on it—because kindness is like chocolate. It's addictive. And when you learn that it really works to make your life more joyous, then you keep it going...

For me, an "experiment" is something you do for a short period of time in order to learn or experience something new. By doing a one-week kindness experiment, you'll likely be able to experience the power of this "technique." As I said on the Oprah Show, simply do two nice things for people around you every day for a week. Then, if you notice that your acts of kindness make you (and the people around you) more joyous, continue your "experiment." It's that simple.

Oprah then asked me for some simple kindness suggestions. I suggested buying a small gift for anyone who looks like they could use some happiness. Yet, the possibilities are endless. Some of my favorite acts of kindness include giving a shoulder massage or empathy to a friend, telling someone what I appreciate about them, or sending someone an emailed article on a subject I know they are interested in. It's fun to come up with new and spontaneous ways to be kind to the people you interact with—whether that be your mate, your kids, or the cashier at the grocery store.

In an age of high-tech wizardry, it can be hard to really "get" that simple acts of kindness can make such a difference in our lives. Yet, if you do a one-week kindness experiment, you'll get to see for yourself. Enjoy!

**Best Suited** for increasing Relationships, Meaning, Pleasure, and Accomplishment.

**Best Features:** Easy to do, quick, powerful, no negative effects, can be done anywhere, helps others, and can lead to greater maturity.

**Possible Shortcomings:** Doesn't help with "root" issues.

# CHAPTER 20

# TAPPING TOWARDS EMOTIONAL FREEDOM

The Emotional Freedom Technique, better known as EFT or "Tapping," is a method for quickly letting go of negative emotions. In case you don't know what it is, I'll briefly describe it, and tell you my personal experience with it. EFT has grown quickly in popularity because it can be done on oneself, and because it can sometimes help people overcome deep-seated psychological issues in a matter of minutes. If after my description you would like to learn more, you can learn how to do the method, step by step (for free) at www.emofree.com.

EFT draws on a variety of theories from various alternative medical modalities, including acupuncture, NLP, energy medicine, and others. It has been used for an extreme variety of psychological and physical conditions. It can be self-administered with some training, or many people go to "expert" EFT practitioners—the way one might go to a therapist. During a typical session, you focus on a specific issue while tapping on "end points of the body's energy meridians." If all goes well, in a matter of a few minutes you can let go of physical ailments (such as a headache or shoulder pain) or psychological distress.

The research that's been done on EFT is not very convincing. Many researchers have denounced its results as simply the result of the placebo effect. However, the placebo effect can be quite strong, and many people have reported dramatic changes in their lives as a result of EFT. It has been my observation that EFT works really well for about one in three people, moderately well for about one in three, and very little for one in three people. I've also noticed that people whose emotions are very available to them tend to respond better than people who are "less emotional."

EFT grew in popularity when some therapists reported curing lifelong phobias and trauma within just a few minutes of its use. To this day, curing phobias and trauma are a popular use of the method. Yet, because you can self-administer EFT, it has been used for everything from relationship problems to changing one's beliefs around money. I've met people who swear by the technique and use it daily for any stressful situation. As for me, I found the method to be just slightly effective, but I am not well trained in the method. When I've gone to an experienced EFT practitioner, I've achieved better results. Although the basic method can be learned in 10 minutes, as with all psychological methods, there are many subtleties that can take years to learn.

The basic theory underpinning EFT is that all negative emotions are a result of a disruption in the body's "energy system." Therefore, by tapping on various acupuncture points while saying what you're distressed about, you can be restored to a state of balance and ease. The basic EFT procedure consists of five simple steps. First, identify an issue that's bothering you, or bothered you in the past. Second, on a one to ten scale (with ten being high), rate how intensely this issue is bothering you. Third, setup a sentence that consists of saying something like, "Even though I have this (briefly name the problem), I deeply and completely accept myself." Fourth, continue to say this sentence while tapping various points on your face, hands, and upper body. Lastly, think of the problem and once again rate how intense the feelings are about it.

Of course, my description is a bit of an oversimplification, but part of the allure of EFT is its simplicity. You can learn the method (from the website I mentioned earlier) and be tapping away in no time. If you're one of the people who immediately notices good results right away, halleluiah! You can then use the method whenever something bothers you. With a bit of time and practice, you'll get even better at it. In addition, EFT can be a great way to help your friends. I've used it a bunch to cure people's headaches, and I find it works about 75% of the time. Even if it doesn't work well for you, it doesn't ever seem to have negative side effects.

If you are one of those people who react well to EFT, you can find endless lessons on how to use it for specific problems on youtube.com. Various EFT practitioners have followings on YouTube, and you can subscribe to their channels for free. I've also found that different EFT practitioners use slightly different methods—so you may find one "flavor" to be more to your liking than another. Watching the video's and seeing dramatic results can be a way to both be inspired and stay motivated in learning the method.

My basic philosophy when it comes to methods is that different things work for different people. I've tried to tell you enough about EFT so that, if you feel curious, you can learn the method for yourself and see what results you get. If you keep trying various methods, you'll eventually find one that really "clicks" for you. As with tens of thousands of other people, perhaps it will be EFT.

**Best Suited** for increasing Pleasure, enhancing Relationships, and creating a sense of Accomplishment.

**Best Features:** Quickness, no negative effects, can be used on any issue, can affect the body, mind, and emotions, improves with practice, and can be used to help others.

**Possible Shortcomings**: Can take a while to learn, not invisible to others, and may not lead to a noticeable effect on some people.

# CHAPTER 21

# THE SPIRITUAL INTIMACY EXPERIENCE

In my book *Life's Big Questions* I have a chapter called "The Spiritual Intimacy Experience." It consists of fifteen questions that partners can ask each other to develop a deeper connection. I received many letters from people stating that answering these questions with their mate led to the most profound experience of intimacy they had ever had. In workshops I lead, I've seen that even when complete strangers openly share their responses to these questions with each other, a beautiful sense of bonding is created.

To enjoy the fruits of the "spiritual intimacy" experience, all you need is a willing partner, about forty-five minutes of time, and a somewhat quiet and private location. You can do this exercise with a lover, parent, child, friend, co-worker, or even a new acquaintance. Yet, since it leads to a deep level of sharing, make sure you do it with someone you'd like to be closer to. Below, you will find the instructions and the fifteen questions. Before you begin the process, make sure you have plenty of time, and are in the mood to fully open and connect with another human being.

## INSTRUCTIONS:

You are about to begin an extended sharing experience. Really getting to know another person involves a learnable set of skills and attitudes, risk-taking, trust, and acceptance. The following questions are designed to assist you in getting to know another person on a fairly intimate level. They can be answered to whatever degree of self-disclosure you wish. Take as long as you like to answer each question. Once you're done, ask the same question of your partner, and let him or her respond while you carefully listen.

When you're the one asking the question, feel free to ask related questions that might further clarify or expand upon your partner's initial response. If a conversation naturally unfolds from your partner's response, that's perfectly all right as well. Once both of you have answered the first question, proceed to the next. If you give this exercise enough time and sincerity, I think you'll find it to be a very satisfying and powerful experience.

The Questions: (take turns answering each one).

1. When are you the happiest?
2. What is your greatest strength?
3. What is your greatest weakness?
4. What was the most difficult time in your life?
5. What is extremely important to you?
6. When do you feel most affectionate?
7. What are you avoiding right now?
8. What helps you to feel really loved?
9. What is the thing you most regret having done?
10. How do you think I see you?

11. What is your heart longing for?
12. What do you consider to be your greatest accomplishment?
13. What was your first impression of me?
14. What do you like best about me?
15. What kind of person have you dreamed of becoming?

Besides being a great way to get to know someone at a deeper level, this exercise also demonstrates a process by which relationships can become more intimate. When we ask a friend or partner meaningful questions, it opens the door for a more profound level of connection with him or her. Most people hunger to talk about important topics such as the ones represented by these questions. Asking "big questions" is a simple and effective way to know the heart of another person—and experience your own essence as well.

Yet, asking good questions is only half the story. The depth to which you can truly listen to your partner in a non-judgmental manner will determine the experience you have in this exercise. Try to listen with an open heart and a quiet mind. If you enjoy this exercise, feel free to make up your own questions. As long as you create an atmosphere of safety and warmth, people appreciate the opportunity to talk about themselves. In our fast paced world of superficiality and hype, the spiritual intimacy experience can be a great way to share the wonders of being human with someone you care about.

**Best Suited** for increasing Relationships, Meaning, and Engagement.

**Best Features:** Powerful, leads to greater maturity, and easy to do and learn.

**Possible Shortcomings:** Takes about 45 minutes, requires a partner, and can only be done a few times without being repetitive.

# CHAPTER 22

# THE GRATITUDE VISIT

For many decades, the field of psychology was focused on how to make mentally sick people feel a *little* bit better. Then, it became focused on how to help people with mild emotional problems get back to normal. But only recently has there been a significant movement in psychology on how to help *normal* people live even happier and more fulfilling lives. Dr. Marty Seligman (mentioned earlier) is the leader of this field that is often referred to as Positive Psychology. One of Dr. Seligman's many contributions has been to test various techniques to see if any of them can dramatically increase a person's level of happiness over a long period of time. Fortunately, a couple of the techniques he's created and tested *have* worked surprisingly well. One of those methods is outlined in this chapter, but before describing the technique, I want to share a story…

Once upon a time, there was a very depressed teenage boy named Roy. Roy hardly spoke to anyone. He spent his days at school feeling overwhelmed and depressed. He even seriously thought of ways of committing suicide. Luckily, Roy had an English teacher named Mr. Downing. Mr. Downing had a big heart, and he could see that Roy was in trouble. One day Mr. Downing asked Roy to stay after class and join him for lunch. With hesitation, Roy carefully accepted. During the lunch, Mr. Downing asked Roy a lot of questions, like what was troubling him, and how he might be of help.

Mr. Downing told Roy that he thought he was a very smart and special kid, and gave him a lot of encouragement. Because of his talk with Mr. Downing, Roy put off his plans to kill himself. Eventually Roy graduated from Jr. High and never thanked Mr. Downing—that is until 25 *years* later. By then Roy had changed his name and had become a bestselling author and seminar leader. More important, he was now a happy person. As you may have guessed, *my* name used to be *Roy* Robinson. I changed it to *Jonathan* in my twenties because I felt like such a different person from who I used to be.

The best part of this story is that I *did* finally thank Mr. Downing for how his act of kindness changed my life. Twenty-five years after I had left his English class, I wrote him a detailed letter reminding him of what he did for me as a teenager, and how it affected my life. Then, with a little effort, I tracked his phone number down, called him up and asked if I could give him something that related to his 1972 English class.

Mr. Downing wasn't sure if he remembered exactly who I was, but he said it would be fine to come over to his house to visit. I went to his house, and once I was inside, I told him a bit more about who I was. Then I read him the letter I'd written that detailed *exactly* what he had done for me in my time of need, and how his kindness had possibly saved my life. As I finished the letter, we were both teary eyed. He told me that my letter was one of the *best* gifts he'd ever received from anyone. For several days, our encounter filled me with a warm glow.

At the time I delivered this letter, I didn't know about Marty Seligman or the Positive Psychology movement. But it ends up that Dr. Seligman, in trying various ways to increase people's level of happiness, had stumbled upon what he began to call the Gratitude Visit. The Gratitude Visit is exactly what I had done with my English teacher, Mr. Downing. It's a way of thanking someone who has impacted your life in a positive way. This is how Dr. Seligman describes the exercise:

*The Gratitude Visit involves three basic steps: First, think of someone who has done something important and wonderful for you, yet who has not been properly thanked. Next, reflect on the benefits you received from this person, and write a letter expressing your gratitude for all he or she did for you. Finally, arrange to deliver the letter personally, and spend some time with this person talking about what you wrote.*

Dr. Seligman has studied the subject of happiness for decades. You can learn more about his ideas by reading his book *Authentic Happiness,* or by going to his website http://www.authentichappiness.sas.upenn.edu.

On his website, he has a lot of good stuff, including various questionnaires that can measure how happy you are with different aspects of your life. It's a great website and worth checking out. Anyway, as I mentioned before, he's also done a lot of research on what *truly* leads to happiness, and what does not. For example, he's shown that more money has almost no effect on one's level of happiness—*unless* you're poor, and that things like beauty, youth, and intelligence also don't seem to lead to happiness. If our culture really understood the implications of his research, the advertising business would probably *collapse*.

No one knows why the Gratitude Visit has such a dramatic effect in lifting someone's spirit. Research shows that it not only lifts your level of happiness *that* day, but its effect has been shown to last a full month— with no negative side effects. That's powerful medicine. If only antidepressants were that effective! Now that you've read this far, I have a question for you: Who would you want to write a letter to? What would you want to tell this person? Even just contemplating such a letter and/or visit can make you feel better. Of course, if you want to experience the full benefits of this technique, you'll have to write the letter, and if possible, deliver it in person.

To help you out, I have a few pointers that may be of help. First, think of *anyone* who you'd like to thank for impacting your life in a positive way. It could be a coach, a minister, a parent, a friend, or even an employer. It's best if the person you choose is someone you could potentially meet face to face sometime in the next month. Second, when you begin your letter, simply state *why* you're writing your letter and what he or she did that you're grateful for. Give details about how his or her kindness has impacted your life in various ways. Then, if possible, do whatever it takes to arrange a face-to-face meeting.

I know it's not easy to arrange a face to face meeting. Yet, it's a hundred times better than a phone call—and don't even *think* about email. When contacting the person you've written a letter to, it's best if you can be a bit *vague* as to why you're wanting to get together. The Gratitude Visit is even more fun when it's a surprise to the person receiving it. When you're face to face with your recipient, say that you have an important letter to read to them. Make sure they're not distracted with other things, and when the time is right, read the letter slowly and with feeling. Savor the experience for a while, and if it feels right, feel free to talk about what you wrote.

I don't know if this experience sounds like much to you, but the reality of it can be very heart opening and powerful. The Gratitude Visit is a dramatic way to show someone you care, but you're also welcome to express gratitude to people in smaller ways. For instance, you can write a note to a waitress saying you appreciate her great service. You can send an email to a friend briefly stating how he or she has positively impacted your life. You can write a little love note to your mate expressing your gratitude for something nice that was done for you.

All these little notes of gratitude help to bring the *spirit* of appreciation and thankfulness into your daily life, and that always feels good. A lot of times, the resistance we feel in doing something like this is mostly at the beginning. Think of exercise. Often you resist it, but once you're working out, it sometimes even feels good.

My bet is that if you start this letter of gratitude, you'll soon find yourself enjoying the process. Then, if you can, arrange to meet with this person sometime in the next month or so, and read your letter directly to them. You'll be glad you did. Take note if this little exercise gives you a bit of a lift in life. If you're like most people, you'll be surprised to find that it does indeed have a *noticeable* effect.

**Best Suited** for increasing Meaning, Relationships, Pleasure, and a sense of Accomplishment.

**Best Features:** Powerful, can help and affect others, and can lead to greater maturity.

**Possible Shortcomings**: Takes a lot of time and effort.

## SECTION FOUR

# LIFE ENHANCING HAPPY APPS

**"Brain surgery? I have an app for that!"**

The Internet and smartphones have greatly impacted our lives in countless ways. Yet, only recently have they had much of an effect on how we pursue happiness. When we think of being happy, we think of travel, spending time with friends, and laughing. We don't necessarily think of smartphones, apps, and surfing the Internet. Yet, the combination of apps and the Internet have created some intriguing possibilities for new ways to pursue feeling good. Some of my personal favorites are in this section. Perhaps you'll be inspired to check some of them out after reading my descriptions.

At the current pace of change happening in the world of apps and the Internet, by the time you read my words some of what I say may be outdated—even if you read what I wrote just three months after I wrote it! That just goes to show how fast things are progressing. An app that I currently describe as "cumbersome" may be as easy as blinking your eye by the time you read my words.

Eventually, all these apps may turn into one life-enhancing super intelligent "coach." Imagine a Siri on steroids who can listen in and learn about you and your life, then tell you with great certainty what you could do to ensure even greater life satisfaction for yourself. Sound farfetched? Last year, I met with a start-up trying to formulate such an artificial intelligent "coach" bent on making us happier. In addition, in 2014 I met with Google executives who talked to me about the progress they're making in developing such a system. Might we someday become passive puppets to this coach who seems to know more about how to make us happier than we do? The future of happiness is a strange world to think about...

For better or worse, until we reach that day where we have a perfect artificial intelligent coach, *we* have to decide how to pursue our own happiness. As the options explode, it's easy to feel overwhelmed and simply stay with the tried and true of what we've known in the past.

However, this is not necessarily a good option either. The times we live in are always changing. Part of our job of seeking joy is to always be exploring what currently adds meaning, depth, and connection to our lives. Just because video games really *worked* for you in the past does not necessarily mean they are what *do it* for you now.

In this section, I cover many different types of apps, from staying amazingly grateful, to finding your soul mate. As with the rest of this book, feel free to read about the category of apps that most appeal to you. Having played with a lot of apps a few years ago and then mostly given up on them, I was surprised at how much better they had gotten when I recently went back to researching them for this book. Finding an app that fits your needs and works for you can be a bit of a project, but once you find one, it can be life changing. Whether you seek a new love, a new body, or a happier disposition, you'll find apps that can help lead the way.

# CHAPTER 23

# HAPPIFY YOUR BLUES GOODBYE

In my book, *Find Happiness Now*, I list 50 different methods that people can do in under three minutes that can help them to feel happier. While the methods work exceedingly well, there's a problem: the methods only work if you use them. Trying to use a method you learn in a book can be, well, trying. We are all so overwhelmed with stuff to do that it can be damn near impossible to remember to use a method that you read about last week. The solution? Happiness apps. There are a lot of apps that, by providing simple suggestions, mood tracking, and reminders, can help you to use the tools they offer.

Thanks to the burgeoning field of Positive Psychology, researchers now have a pretty good idea of what truly makes people feel happy and fulfilled. The various apps I review in this section all use this data to motivate you to do simple activities that are known to lead to greater joy, peace, and happiness. Some of the apps focus on just one activity—such as gratitude, whereas others provide a whole smorgasbord of suggestions. I suggest that after you read about the apps I review in this section that you decide to try out the ones that sound best to you. If an app works to improve your life—great! If it just becomes a burden, then try another. Eventually you'll find the app that, like Goldilocks once said—feels "just right."

**1. Happify**: Happify is a major player in the field of "happy apps." It has a lot of games and activities, and a lot of "tracks" you can do to improve your happiness level. In addition, for $5 a month for a year, you get access to a lot more tracking, games, and activities on both your mobile device and computer.

One of the advantages of Happify is that it gives you so much stuff to choose from. They have separate tracks called, "Savor, Aspire, Empathize, Thank, and Victorious Self." All these options can also be a disadvantage if you crave a simple, easy to navigate app. Perhaps my favorite feature of Happify is that it basically can pester you to take stock of the positive things in your life. According to Positive Psychology research, this is a major boon if you want to be happier. The creators of Happify say that Happify users are happy with Happify. Evidently they say users report an 86% increase in happiness over two months. If you're willing to dive in to this deep and interesting app, you will likely find some good benefits.

**2. Talkspace**: Talkspace is an interesting new app and approach to therapy. Basically, for $25 a week, you get to have unlimited text messages to a licensed mental health professional. Their tagline is, "Therapy for how we live today." While there is no peer reviewed research on how Talkspace compares to traditional therapy, it does have a lot of people who think it's fantastic. For one thing, it can cost a lot less than traditional therapy. Secondly, your therapist will usually reply to your text in just a few minutes—a lot faster than it takes to schedule a time to meet with a traditional therapist in an office.

Once you sign up for Talkspace, you're sent a list of questions. By answering these, it helps the people at Talkspace to pair you up with an appropriate therapist to meet your specific needs. If you can afford $25 a week and the idea of a "therapist on demand" appeals to you, then Talkspace is worthy of a test ride.

**3. Moodkit**: Moodkit is an app based on the model of therapy known as Cognitive Behavioral Therapy, or CBT for short. CBT has been shown to be a very effective form of therapy, and is based on how correcting distortions in our thinking can help us to feel better. It is particularly useful for people who suffer from anxiety and depression.

The app costs $4.99 and provides users with over 150 mood boosting activities, along with a way to journal your thoughts. Once you write down a thought, the app helps you see which of several "cognitive distortions" may be affecting your thinking and mood. It's a useful tool for helping make sure your mind doesn't take you down a dark and lonely road.

**4. Happier:** Happier is free, easy, and has science to back up that it really works. You need a Facebook account to use it, but that also lets you easily (if you want) share your posts with your Facebook friends. At the heart of Happier is the suggestion that you briefly describe (or upload a picture) that includes three happy moments from each day. The thinking behind this is that sharing happy moments significantly increases your happiness level over time. In Chapter 19, I describe this method in more detail. Unfortunately, in the Happier app, they don't have you ask yourself, "Why did this good thing happen?" Yet, according to the research, that's a major reason why the "3 Good Things" exercise is so effective in boosting one's happiness level.

Besides the fact the app is nicely focused and easy to use, I like how it offers up to three reminders a day for asking you about "happy moments." Such reminders are truly useful if you want to make sure you keep track of the positive events in your life. *Time* magazine named

Happier as one of the best apps of 2013. Its focus on sharing things with a community can be another motivating factor for sticking to its simple, but effective focus.

**5. Kindr**: Kindr is a great way to pass on two second videos—along with an appropriate message—to your friends. You can find hundreds of cute, meaningful, or funny videos that, when sent to a friend, are a way of showing that you're thinking of them. Categories of videos include: Celebrations, Thank You, Sorry, Congratulations, Birthday, Reactions, Complements, and Funny.

What I like about Kindr is that it makes it so easy to connect with your friends in a meaningful way. I have included it in this section on happiness apps because small acts of kindness are the number one way to boost *your own* level of happiness (see Chapter 20). I notice that whenever I go through the list of Kindr videos and think about sending a nice message to a friend, it makes me happier. As a bonus, my friends who have received my video and message really appreciate it too. It's a win-win of happiness. Any method for boosting happiness that's free, immediately feels good, is good for you, and makes other's happier is definitely worth checking out.

**Best Suited** for increasing Pleasure, Meaning, and a sense of Accomplishment.

**Best Features**: Low or no cost; can be done anywhere; can lead to greater emotional maturity; and can be very effective.

**Possible Shortcomings**: Doesn't deal with root issues, and some are clunky to use.

# CHAPTER 24

# THE DANCE OF RELATIONSHIP ENHANCEMENT

According to Positive Psychology researchers, the most important key for being happy is the quality and quantity of your relationships. If you have lots of friends, or if your connection with your intimate partner is going particularly well, you're likely a happy camper. On the other hand, even if you're wealthy and healthy—if your relationships suck—you will likely be pretty miserable. That being the case, it's worth looking at what apps have consistently been rated as helpful to creating great relationships.

I will briefly review five apps that have been both popular and highly recommended as being beneficial to intimate relationships. Many of these apps suggest creative ways to stay connected, share special times together, or even overcome relationship challenges. In this age of too much to do, a relationship enhancing app can act as a reminder of what's really important. It can help make your significant other a priority where it really counts—in your daily actions—with a little help from your smartphone.

**Couple**: This is one of the most popular apps for couples, and for good reason. It attempts to do just about everything, and it does it pretty well. Using Couple, you can send private videos, photos, doodles, stickers, and voice messages. There's a shared calendar so you can better schedule things with your partner, and there's even suggestions for date night. This app allows you to easily stay constantly connected with your mate, and even keeps all your memories on a shared timeline. One fun feature of Couple is called "Thumbkiss." This allows you to touch your phones simultaneously and leave a thumbprint on top of each other—while your phone vibrates in response to your "thumb hug." If you're looking for an app that does a bit of everything, you can do no wrong by trying out Couple. It has over two million downloads and has won an Apple Editor's choice award.

**Avocado**: Avocado lets you communicate easily about the day-to-day stuff. You can set up to-do lists and get instant sync of items you've completed. You can also exchange notes and memos, keep your Google calendars updated and synced, and add fun to your communication with self-made emoticons of your own photos. Avocado can also be a simple way to keep an archive of your relationship. It has a simple User Interface, and its focus on syncing schedules with your partner make it attractive for staying connected easily.

**The Icebreak**: This app is focused on creating more meaningful conversations between you and your significant other. It includes a list of questions you can ask your partner—or answer anonymously with the Icebreak community. One nice feature is something where you are encouraged to capture "today's moment," with a photo of something that amazed you today. Although many people use this app to get to better know a potentially new romantic partner, I found the questions work well even if you've been a couple for a long time.

A unique feature of The Icebreak is each time you complete one of the app's actions, you receive $10 in Icebreak coins. When you earn $500 in coins, you get a 20% discount (up to $20) at participating businesses.

**Between:** Between allows you to easily create an intimate space where you and your partner exchange and store photos, voice messages, stickers, and animated emoticons. The app reached one million downloads within a year after launching, partly because the app is rather addictive. Current users spend 300 minutes a month on average on it—helping to build a digital connection that creates a sense of shared experience.

As with Couple, Between does a bit of everything. Many people liked its User Interface more than Couple, but it's a matter of personal preference. Once in use, it really does help to create a "sacred digital space" that only you and your partner share. For forgetful people (like me), its reminders about important dates and anniversaries can definitely be helpful to the health of your relationship!

**Fix a Fight**: Well, if all these other apps aren't working for you, there is always "Fix a Fight." This app suggests proven ways to communicate better, make-up after a fight, and initiate discussions about things that bother you—without getting into a fight in the first place. In addition, the app includes a list of relaxation and self-calming exercises for both you and your partner to use to calm down. All this advice is provided by Mark McGonigle—a renowned psychotherapist and relationship expert.

As the author of *Communication Miracles for Couples*, I know that relationship breakdowns are both painful and preventable. When my book became a bestseller, I ended up doing a lot of counseling with couples. I soon saw that couples tend to make the same two or three mistakes over and over again. These "mistakes" in communication and relationships can often be easily remedied if you're willing to take the time to read a book (hint, hint!), or download an app that can help you. I suggest that you not wait until things are bad between you and your partner. A little bit of knowledge and prevention can save yourself from a lot of grief. Now is the time to invest in your intimate relationship through one of these apps—or my *Communication Miracles* book. A good intimate relationship is one of the best time tested paths to more joy in life.

**Best Suited** for improving Relationships, Engagement, and Meaning.

**Best Features:** Low or no cost, can lead to greater emotional connection, can help your partner feel good, and relatively easy to use.

**Possible Shortcomings:** Effect is subtle at first, doesn't deal with root issues, and takes some time to learn how to use.

# CHAPTER 25

# LOOKING FOR MODERN LOVE

In his bestselling book, *Modern Romance*, comedian Aziz Ansari discusses how finding a romantic partner has changed dramatically over the last few decades. It used to be that people's choices were few, so they married early—and often to someone who lived within a mile of them. Nowadays, thanks to the Internet and dating apps, people's choices are almost infinite. Learning how to navigate this new world of online dating can be stressful, but if you can find the love of your life, it's well worth the effort.

As of 2015, fully one-third of people getting married originally met through an online dating service—and the numbers are growing each year. Studies show that one's happiness level is deeply impacted by being in a good relationship, so it's worth seeing how the latest dating app might help you to find your perfect partner. Of course, there's a learning curve in knowing how to best use the Internet and apps to get what you're looking for. Yet, once you find a site or app that works for you, you may be well on your way to finding the love of your life.

In this chapter, I'll briefly mention several popular dating apps, including how they operate and who they are best suited for. But before doing that, some words of advice: While dating apps can give you more choices and more dates, they can't magically create connection. People who think that an app's technology will find them the love they seek are bound to be sorely disappointed. Dating apps simply provide lots of choices, convenience, and some initial help in bringing potential partners together. The rest is up to you and your ability to connect with someone, your relationship skills, and that mysterious thing known as "chemistry." That being said, what follows is a brief description of several popular dating apps that may make your search for modern love a bit easier:

**1. Tinder**: This app has become enormously popular because it is so easy to set up, use, and so many people are using it. Once you log in with your Facebook account, everything Tinder needs to know about you is automatically imported. With a simple "swipe" with your thumb, you can let the people who pop up on your screen know if you're interested. Only if they subsequently express an interest in you can a messaging dialogue begin. This app is good for ease of use and the fact that it spares you from feeling that others are rejecting you.

**2. Coffee Meets Bagel** and **Hinge**: These apps look at your mutual Facebook friends and curate a match based on your mutual interests and friends. If you both say "yes" to a meeting, then the apps connect you to each other so you can take it from there. If you're into finding a partner with mutual friends and interests, these apps are a good place to begin.

**3. Hitch**: This app works on the premise that your friends can be helpful in setting you up with someone they think is a good match for you. In this app, your Facebook friends can suggest dates for you, or you can play matchmaker for your friends. As with other apps that rely on

Facebook friends, once some interest is expressed by both parties, your relationship skills need to take over.

**4. Okcupid:** This app, like its web-based version, focuses on predicting how good of a match you are with someone else—based on extensive profile questions. It also has a huge user base, so there are plenty of people you can see and evaluate by reading about them. In addition, their algorithms for predicting who you'll like are, I am told, pretty damn good.

**5. Match.com:** This app has an enormous user base, and sends prospective matches to your inbox on a daily basis. In an attempt to keep up with the changing dating scene, it offers a new feature called Stream for checking out nearby matches, and a Tinder-like feature for sending a "like" or "pass" on potential dates.

Besides these and other similar dating apps, there are plenty of apps that focus on a specialized population of people. For example, if you only want to date Christians, Christianmingle.com is available. If you're Jewish, Jdate.com awaits you. Whether you're into kink, polyamory, dating after 70 or whatever you like, it's all there somewhere on the web. Like money, technology can't get you love, but it can give you intelligent choices that may make finding love a lot easier.

**Best Suited** for improving your Relationships, Pleasure, and Meaning.

**Best Features:** Most are easy to use, can be done anywhere, you tend to improve with practice, and are low or no cost.

**Possible Shortcomings**: It takes a while to find a suitable match, and finding a partner does not automatically help you with your "issues."

# CHAPTER 26

# THE ATTITUDE OF GRATITUDE

Back in 1995 when I interviewed 40 spiritual leaders for my book *The Experience of God*, I was surprised by how many people suggested that gratitude was their *best* way of connecting with a sacred reality. People ranging from Oprah Winfrey to the Dalai Lama all said that practicing gratitude was a major key to their well-being and helpful in their spiritual path.

Having heard about the powerful possibilities of a daily gratitude practice, I was on the lookout for ways to help me feel more thankful. Then, one day a friend told me about an Indian guru who supposedly had a magical mantra for helping people feel overwhelming gratitude. I wanted to know his technique, so I booked a flight to India, took a rickshaw for three hours, and finally landed at this guru's ashram. After waiting in line four hours to talk to this holy man, I finally got a chance to ask him about his magical mantra for feeling more gratitude.

The guru looked me over, then with a deep Indian accent said, "Yes, my mantra is the most powerful mantra on Earth." He told me to come close, so I leaned in next to him. I was very excited. Then, the holy man put his mouth close to my ear and whispered to me, "Whenever possible, repeat the following words in your head. The mantra I give you are the words..."

By now I was so excited that I literally stopped breathing so I could make sure I heard the magical words correctly. After a brief pause, the guru finally said, "...the words are...*thank you*."

I was stunned. At first I thought he was joking, but as I looked up at him, he wasn't smiling. I stared at him for a moment and then practically shouted, "Thank you!? I traveled 18,000 miles to hear the words 'thank you'? *That's it*?!"

The guru said, "No, '*that's it*' is the mantra you *have* been using and *that* mantra makes you feel like you never have enough. My mantra is 'thank you'—not 'that's it!' 'That's it' will take you *nowhere*, but 'thank you' will quiet your mind and open your heart. But you must say it many, many times a day for each blessing in your life, and you must say it from your heart. So when you eat good food, say thank you. When you see your child or a sunset or your pet, say thank you and soon you will feel overwhelming gratitude."

Well, I was pretty pissed off and disappointed, but having traveled all that distance I figured I would try out what he said. As I left the ashram, I found a taxi and fortunately, the taxi had air conditioning. As I stepped into the car, I said a silent thank you to the Universe for giving me this blessing. Then, back at my hotel room, I took a shower. As the water cleaned my sweaty body, I said another thank you from my heart. Then I turned on the TV, and realized this free entertainment also deserved a thank you. I kept saying a silent "thank you" from my heart for each thing I encountered. Within 30 minutes, I literally had tears of gratitude going down my face as I tuned into the world of abundance we all have. It was like entering a parallel universe.

From that experience, I vowed to practice my magical mantra technique in daily life. Yet, I soon learned that new habits are hard to maintain unless you have help from a person or a gadget. Fortunately, there are many apps that can help you maintain a daily gratitude practice. Studies show that a daily or even weekly gratitude practice significantly increases your level of happiness—so they're definitely worth a try.

As with any app, you need to try out a couple and see which one feels like the best fit for you. Here's a brief description of five of my favorites:

**1. Gratitude Journal**: This one is the leader in the field. Part of its popularity is its simplicity. It asks you to identify 5 things you're grateful for each day. You can also rate your day and snap photos to put into your journal.

**2. Thankful For:** This one is even simpler than Gratitude Journal, and it also includes inspirational quotes. Yet, it doesn't have all the bells and whistles of some of the other gratitude apps.

**3. Live Happy**: This app is based on the research of Positive Psychology researcher Sonja Lyubomirsky. It consists of several different happiness boosting activities, including a good section on increasing gratitude. It also aims to educate users as to why certain activities boost happiness.

**4. The Gratitude Habit**: This is not really a typical app. Instead, it's an animated lecture about a simple technique for feeling happier. The technique is basically the "Three Good Things" method I outlined in Chapter 19. If you want to use that method, this app can walk you through the how and the why.

**5. Gratitude Journal 365**: This updated form of Gratitude Journal allows you to share your entries via social networking, take daily pictures, and allows you to record progress towards your goals.

If you try out a couple of these apps, you'll see they are pretty similar. Yet, small dissimilarities can be the difference between using an app on a daily basis, and letting it lie lonely on your smartphone. With hundreds of studies showing that a practice of daily gratitude can be a big happiness booster, these apps are worth checking out. People who use them often report dramatic increases in their level of joy, peace, and happiness.

**Best Suited** for increasing a sense of Meaning, feeling good about Relationships, and experiencing a sense of Accomplishment.

**Best Features:** No cost, easy to do, can be done anywhere, improves with practice, can lead to more maturity, and can affect the body, mind, and emotions.

**Possible Shortcomings:** The effect is usually not immediately powerful, and it doesn't deal with "root" issues.

# CHAPTER 27

# SLEEP YOUR WAY TO SUCCESS

How did you sleep last night? If you're like a lot of Americans, the answer is, "not so well." Fully 40% of Americans don't get enough sleep, 25% takes pills to fall asleep, and 10% are chronic insomniacs. According to the Center for Disease Control, insufficient sleep is associated with a number of chronic diseases, such as diabetes, heart disease, obesity, and depression. In addition, it has been shown that a lack of sleep leads to lower job satisfaction and less innovation. But the good news is studies show that some simple changes in one's sleep schedule can lead to a 20% increase in productivity in the workplace, and a happier and healthier life. Getting a good night's sleep is the foundation for a life of joy, health, and achievement.

The best sleep trackers are ones that you wear on your head or arm when you go to bed, but these cost about $100. There are dozens of apps to help you fall asleep or "achieve" a deeper experience of sleep, yet most of them have similar features. Perhaps the best and most popular is Sleepbot. Like other sleep apps, it has a motion tracker to track how much you toss and turn, an automatic sound recorder to record any sound you make, and something called a "smart" alarm.

A smart alarm is simply an alarm that aims to wake you up while you are in a lighter stage of sleep. In the app, you select a 30 minute "window" as to when you'd like to wake up. Then the app decides (based on your movements) when would be the best time in that 30 minute window to awaken you. You can also program the app to wake you up with any song that you have in iTunes. In addition to a motion tracker, sound recorder, and smart alarm, many sleep apps also have ways to keep track of how long you've spent in deep vs. light sleep, and ways to see your progress (or lack thereof) over time.

The accuracy of these free or almost free sleep apps is questionable. If you want a more precise view of your sleep patterns, you'll need to wear something on your arm or face to get a more accurate picture. However, apps such as Sleepbot or Sleep Cycle do make you more aware of your sleep patterns, and the result of increased awareness is often a better quality sleep.

If your primary problem is falling asleep, there are apps specially designed for that. The app known as "Relax Melodies" uses binaural beats (see Audio Meditators in High Tech Tools section) to help induce sleepiness. If you suffer from occasional insomnia, it's definitely worth a try. There is also "Relax and Sleep Well" by hypnotist Glenn Harold that gets rave reviews from many people. In this app, Glen's soothing voice gently hypnotizes you into a restful night's sleep. Many people swear by these simple ways to help unwind and get to sleep. It certainly beats getting hooked on sleeping pills.

Personally, I'd like to see an app that combines *all* the features mentioned in this section into a single app. As of this writing (2016), I'm not aware of such a thing. Yet, depending on your sleeping challenge, the individual apps here can definitely be helpful. I've used them, and they have both helped me to fall asleep more easily, and given me new information about my sleep patterns. For instance, I used to think that coffee didn't disrupt my sleep, but by seeing a pattern of "charting" less deep sleep each time I drank coffee during the day, I was convinced that it wasn't a good drug for me. Also, by keeping track of my sleep patterns, I soon learned that I slept *better* when I went to bed later.

As with most apps, there is a bit of a learning curve in discovering what app most suits your needs, as well as getting it set up just right for you. Yet, sleep is one of those things that is worth a little scrutiny. We spend a third of our life asleep, and if that third is not "fulfilling," the other two-thirds of our life tends to not go well either. So, if your sleep could use an upgrade, try out one of these apps and see what they can do for you.

**Best Suited** for increasing your Pleasure and Accomplishment.

**Best Features:** Can help with various life issues, can affect body, mind, and emotions, improves with practice, low cost, and no negative side effects.

**Possible Shortcoming**: Can take a while to notice an effect, and takes a bit to learn how to interpret the apps or devices.

# CHAPTER 28

# MEDITATION MADE TO ORDER

When I was sixteen years old, I took the Transcendental Meditation course. My mother was very much against it—since she thought meditation was for hippies and weirdos. I told her, "Someday even your *doctor* will tell you that you should meditate every day." She laughed at my pronouncement. About forty years later, I got an excited call from my mother. She said to me, "Guess what my doctor told me I need to do every day? Meditate!"

I replied, "Victory at last!" We both laughed. It was a sweet moment.

Meditation has definitely gone mainstream. It has been on the cover of *Time*, and it has been proven to reduce stress, make people happier, make people more productive at work, and even improve one's health and length of life. Unfortunately, there is a problem. Meditation involves quieting your mind, and if you've ever tried meditating, you may have noticed that your mind is completely out of control and it never shuts up! What to do? Luckily, there are many great apps you can get for free or low cost that will help you to meditate.

Although listening to a guided meditation is not the same as meditating on your own, it tends to be much easier to do for beginners. In this way, meditation apps can act as “training wheels,” helping you learn what a quiet mind feels like. Then, once you feel you got the hang of it, you may choose to venture out on your own and find a technique you’d like to explore without the aid of an app.

Most of the meditation apps that are popular consist of a variety of guided meditations, soothing music, and beautiful pictures. Yet, in a crowded field, they each are targeted towards different needs, and some have very unique features to explore. In the following section I will briefly review six of the most popular meditation apps. Perhaps one of them will call out to you. If so, download it and give it a test ride.

So…in no particular order, here is a brief description of five popular meditation apps:

**1. Headspace:** Headspace is probably the best-known meditation app, with an extremely large number of users. It is billed as “your very own personal trainer, here to help train your mind.” Besides the usual features of lots of guided meditations, it has a buddy system and animations to help with motivation. You can also download meditations for offline use, and find very specialized guided meditations—such as ones for eating or being on public transportation.

**2. Buddhify2:** Buddhify2 is billed as “urban meditation,” meaning it specializes in meditation for people on the go. It is very user friendly, and it includes a two-player meditation mode and an ability to track your progress. You can also specify the style and length of the meditation session you would like to experience.

**3. Calm:** Calm consistently gets high reviews because people like the music, narrator, and nature scenes. As with most meditation apps, there are a lot of choices when it comes to time length and the focus of the meditation session.

**4. Equanimity:** Equanimity includes the somewhat unique features of an ability to keep a journal and a way to help you stay motivated. In addition, it has a rather sophisticated analytics features so that you can carefully track your progress.

**5. Omvana:** Omvana has a large library of recordings, everything from shedding pounds to revitalizing your sex life. In addition, it connects to Healthkit on the iPhone. By having this connection, it can automatically suggest meditations based on your stress level.

Finding the right meditation app for you consists of some trial and error. Fortunately, you can try several—since most are free or a nominal cost. Once you find one that feels right, you have a dandy little friend for life. In any situation, you can find a guided meditation to take you from stressed-out to joyed-out in just a few minutes. That's a really good deal.

**Best Suited** for increasing all five of the "PERMA" happiness factors—depending on what types of guided meditations you listen to, and what your focus is.

**Best Features:** Easy, quick, powerful, for any issue, improves with practice, can lead to greater maturity, no negative side effects, and can affect body, mind, and emotions.

**Possible Shortcomings:** Takes some time to find the app/guided meditations that feel "just right."

SECTION FIVE

# ALTERNATIVE ENERGY METHODS

"SEE IF OUR TECHNICAL PEOPLE CAN GET THIS UP AND RUNNING."

Ever since I was a teenager, I've been interested in things that are hard to explain. Whether that be psychic phenomena or the power of being inundated with "crystal energy," I'm fascinated that some things seem to "work," although we don't know how or why. This section is for those of you who are comfortable being called "new age," or maybe even "crackpots." The tools in this section may or may not work for you, but many people swear they have been healed or transformed by their mysterious power.

I find that people tend to be prejudiced against things if they don't feel they know *how* something works. Thus, since there is no clear understanding as to how crystals or orgone accumulators might affect consciousness, most people dismiss them. However, when you think about it, we don't really know how *anything* works. We certainly don't know how our brain produces consciousness, yet we don't dismiss the fact that we have consciousness. So let me provide an overriding explanation for how anything in this section really works.

My theory as to what makes the methods in this section work has to do with a concept abbreviated as P.F.M. which is a term first coined by the U.S. military to describe how ballistic missiles found their targets half way around the world. Later, it was used to describe how the human brain works, as well as your smartphone. P.F.M. is actually a very good description as to how *most* things work when you really understand them in their full complexity. In case you're curious, the letters P.F.M. stand for *Pure Fucking Magic!* When you get right down to it, *that's* what makes most things work, from trees, to love, to human brains. Now you know...you're welcome!

In exploring the methods in this section, you will have to be like a mad scientist and subject yourself to unusual energies. I've found that people who meditate regularly, or who are generally more sensitive tend to react more profoundly to these tools. Yet, you never know until you try. I have a friend who doesn't "believe" in the power of crystals and thinks meditation is for "nerds," but is so affected by the presence of certain crystals in my house that he can't go near them without feeling energy streaming through his body. Thus, belief is not a prerequisite for feeling the power of these tools.

# CHAPTER 29

# ORGONE ACCUMULATORS AND ORGANITE

In the 1970's, I enjoyed a song by a group called Hawkwind whose lyrics went like this:

I've got an orgone accumulator
It makes me feel much greater
I'll see you sometime later
When I'm through with my accumulator
It's no social integrator
It's a one man isolator
It's a back brain stimulator
It's a cerebral vibrator
Those energy stimulators
Just turn your eyeballs into craters
But an orgone accumulator
Is a superman creator

At the time I heard the song, I didn't know what an orgone accumulator was, but it certainly sounded like fun. I did a little research and found out that it was invented by Dr. Wilhelm Reich— a controversial doctor who studied internal energy and the orgasm. With some effort, I learned you can make your own orgone accumulator by stacking alternating layers of wool or cotton with steel wool to form a thick blanket. The theory being that this configuration would accumulate energy from its surroundings and focus it to whoever was lying underneath the blanket. To my amazement, it seemed to work. Lying under my orgone blanket, I would feel a strange, soothing energy permeate deep into my bones.

Later, I learned that its best to use orgone blankets only in natural settings since it picks up *all* energy nearby it—even EMF waves, microwaves, etc. Then, in the year 2000, a couple named Don and Carol Croft created a new type of orgone accumulator. Their intention was to turn an orgone accumulator into a solid object that would transmute negative energy into positive energy. If you want to know more technical details about orgone accumulators or organite, you can go to www. Organite.info.

According to many in the field, organite can not only turn negative energy into positive energy, but it can help plants grow, mitigate the effects of EMF radiation, energize a person, and even help with your mood. I have several pieces of organite that look like thick coasters for drinks. I place my drinking water on these pieces of organite and then drink from those glasses throughout the day. The effect is subtle, but the water both tastes better and seems to nourish me in a deeper way.

Besides being used as water enhancers, organite is sometimes fashioned into pendants or pyramids to help people with EMF radiation—or to just feel better. If you type in "Organite" into Amazon. com, you'll see a lot of things to choose from for very little money.

A friend of mine makes huge (5 foot diameter) organite sculptures that are both beautiful and quite impactful if you sit in front of them. You can literally get "charged up" as you look at them from a couple of feet away. But for most people who want to experiment with orgone accumulators, I recommend starting with an orgone blanket. First, they are relatively easy to make. All you need is a lot of cotton or sheep wool's batting, and thin sheets of steel wool. You can find instructions for making them on the web, such as on this YouTube video: https://www.youtube.com/watch?v=pRCDjUEGyf4. Of course, you can also buy an orgone blanket. An 18" by 24" blanket costs $185 and can be found at http://www.orgonics.com/blankets.htm.

I love my orgone blanket. I made it myself and use it to cover my chest and stomach area when I meditate. As long as I don't have my computer on nearby, it suffuses me with a nice soothing energy. (Remember, orgone accumulators pick up *all* nearby energy, so you don't want to be near a source of EMF waves). I also use it during times that I'm cold or not feeling well to give me an extra boost of healing, warm energy. Some people feel nothing at all, and some find it to be like drinking too much coffee. Your mileage may vary.

While no one has come up with a good theory as to why orgone accumulators work, and despite some studies showing there is a real effect, they are still controversial. Some people have even said that if used near power poles or computer screens, they can make you sick. So, if you're very sensitive to energy, be careful with them. Then again, if you're very sensitive to energy, try one in a natural environment and enjoy the subtle, but internal soothing sensations of a lifetime. Like the song lyrics suggest, you may find your orgone accumulator is a "superman (or woman) creator."

**Best Suited** for increasing Pleasure and Engagement.

**Best Features:** Easy to "do," can help others, and can improve with practice.

**Possible Shortcomings:** Cost, and effects may not be noticeable to some people.

# CHAPTER 30

# SURRENDERING TO YOUR HIGHER POWER

I hesitated to put this chapter in the book, but then I figured that the oldest, most time-tested path for finding joy should definitely be represented here. Although surrendering to your Higher Power is not an app, gadget, or supplement, it *is* a tool. People who have had the experience of feeling the Holy Spirit, or invoking a Hindu deity, or simply surrendering to God as best they can *are* using a tool to find inner peace. The question is, "What are the ways to surrender so fully that some beautiful energy fills you up?" Fortunately, religions and thousands of years of people trying to surrender can give us some clues as to how such surrender happens.

As the author of *The Complete Idiot's Guide to Awakening Your Spirituality*, I researched all the major religions of the world and discovered they all used the "tool" of surrender as part of their practice. The *way* they suggested one surrender, or the *what or who* you were supposed to surrender to varied, but the goal always seemed to be to feel more peace, connection, and love. As I studied and tried various surrender type practices, I saw that there were certain commonalities amongst them. By informing you of what I found, my hope is you'll be better able to explore the art of surrender for yourself.

What follows are descriptions of specific tools that seem to correlate well with people surrendering to higher forces. It's above my pay grade to know how all this works, or to say whether there is really just one Power to surrender to (i.e. God), or many different forces. Since I'm a very practical person, I don't really care that much. If I try something and the result is overwhelming joy, I don't worry whether it was Jesus, Krishna, or my own inner Chi that filled me from within. That being said, I've seen that surrender tends to happen when a person is praying to or focused on a *specific* higher force. You are more likely to have a "surrender experience" if you have a background or relationship with a specific deity—such as Jesus or Shiva— than if you just surrender to the cosmos.

I've also noticed that people have ecstatic surrender experiences more commonly in certain environments. For example, such experiences are more likely to happen in a church, synagogue, or mosque than in your bathroom. This may be because of the group energy of like-minded people or the fact that there is often religious music and prayers happening in such places. It also may be due to the fact that we don't ever think of surrendering in the grocery store, whereas church is set up for creating the conditions of surrender. Whatever the reason, the right building and group of like-minded people, the right music, and appropriate prayers are all helpful in eliciting the surrender experience.

In looking over the times I've felt filled up from within by a higher energy, I would have to say that my level of *sincerity* played a major part. Obviously, you're more likely to feel the grace of God while praying on your knees for help than while balancing your checkbook! In fact, it has often been my feeling of sheer helplessness that has been a doorway for grace to fill me up. For better or worse, you can't fake sincerity.

However, through passionate honesty with yourself, you can better be able to feel the *need* for help. On the other hand, if you always cover up your pain, you'll likely never feel the helplessness that can sometimes trigger a surrender experience.

Just so you know where I'm coming from, I'm rather eclectic in my religious views. At some point in my life, I've considered myself Jewish, Christian, Buddhist, Hindu, and a student of Gurdjieff's Fourth Way school. Yet, while pursuing each of these "systems," I've found that I felt more surrender when I placed my *body* in certain positions. For example, having my palms facing up or my hands in a praying position seemed to help facilitate me surrendering. In some religions, you'll see people with their hands over their head or being prostate on the floor. There is no single "right" surrender position. But with a bit of trial and error, you may find a body position seem to help *you* to fully let go.

Lastly, another similarity I have noticed amongst surrender practices is the tendency for people to sing, to praise a certain deity, and/or practice devotion. All of these practices promote the opening of our hearts, and an open heart (or broken heart) can definitely be an aid in surrender. Devotion is not my forte, but I used to go to a church where that was the whole focus. In fact, the church had no pastor. Instead, the entire service consisted of a rock and roll band that sang songs of devotion and praise to Jesus. To my surprise, I would get so high in this church that I couldn't even move. My body would be filled with joy, and then I would "lose" my body and float ecstatically in a realm of pure loving energy. What made this experience even stranger was that I did not consider myself a Christian at the time! All I can say is, "The Lord works in mysterious ways!"

Surrendering to a power or force bigger than our ego is a mysterious process. Although I have briefly outlined some things that may help in the process, there are no guarantees. Yet, like many things in life, the more you try, the more likely you will succeed. These higher energies are always available. It's something in *ourselves* that block them most of the time. Part of the art of surrender is learning the keys that can help *you* be more receptive to the Grace that is waiting to enter your heart.

**Best Suited** for increasing Meaning, Engagement, and Pleasure.

**Best Features:** Effect can be very powerful, can help with any issue, no cost, improves with practice, and can lead to spiritual maturity.

**Possible Shortcomings:** Can be difficult to experience, can take a long time to experience, and generally can't be done anywhere.

# CHAPTER 31

# THE CRYSTAL CRAZE

I used to have a housemate who was all about crystals. He had about 100 crystals in his room, and he'd place them on client's chakras (energy points along the body) and supposedly "heal" them. I was kind of a New Age guy myself at the time, but his obsession even made *my* eyes roll. After months of his offering me a healing session—I finally relented just so he would shut up. To my surprise, while under his crystal tutelage, I went into a very bizarre and joyful altered state of consciousness. I had to admit, there *was* something to working with crystals.

I am not a crystal expert. In fact, I had to read a book on the subject before writing this chapter so I wouldn't come off as a complete idiot. In general, there are two views of "crystal healing." One view is that anyone who thinks crystals emanate energy and can heal you is, by definition, a crackpot. The second view is that crystal healing is a science that anyone can and should partake in. If you are not firmly in the first camp, then I can give you some basics and pointers about joining the second camp.

The first thing to know about crystals is that there are a lot of different types of crystals—and I mean a lot. Supposedly, they each have their own unique healing properties and energies, and various books can describe in detail how to use each specific type of crystal. According to the book, *Crystal Healing for Beginners*, crystals "act as tuning forks, bringing our energy field back to the level at which (our chakras) vibrate most efficiently." However, for total beginners like me, it is suggested that you can't go wrong with the simplicity of quartz crystals. Whether in a lone cylinder or part of a quartz cluster, these usually clear looking crystals are considered all-purpose energy and health enhancers.

I have a few crystals at home. I'm embarrassed to admit it, but I like holding one in my hand when I meditate. Does it help? It seems to, but the placebo effect can be pretty powerful. However, there is a crystal shop near where I live and my reaction to that is unmistakable. Whenever I go in this shop, my body starts to feel like I just drank *way* too much coffee. The shop probably has 500 crystals in it, and if I'm in there for more than ten minutes, I feel like my head will explode.

When I asked the woman who runs the shop about this, she said, "That's not uncommon for people who are sensitive, but after a while your body gets used to it." So if you want to explore how crystals may help you, go into a crystal shop and see what attracts you. Ask a knowledgeable staff person what each crystal is best suited for, and see if you intuitively connect with one or more crystals. If you want to go further into the crystal healing craze, consider getting a book such as *Crystal Healing for Beginners*.

According to the books and articles I read about crystals, you can literally "program" a crystal to serve a certain purpose for you. This is often done while holding a crystal in one or both hands and saying an affirmation such as "I open to love more and more each day." If you have a specific ailment such as depression or insomnia, you can program a specific crystal to help with that condition. In books you can find lists of how certain crystals help restore balance in specific chakras. For instance, "Azurite has vibrations that enhance the workings of your third eye." Whether any of this is true or not I will leave up to you.

If you happen to be someone who finds crystals very beautiful, or someone who feels their body may explode while browsing in a crystal shop, it's probably worth buying some and playing with them. See if they do anything for you. If they do, keep buying ones that attract you or are known to be good for what ails you. Soon you may have your own collection at home, and if you can consistently feel something from them, you'll have a new pathway to joy. The only negative side effect will be your having to deal with people who roll their eyes at you. But, if you're in joy, at least you won't care…

**Best Suited** for increasing your Pleasure and Meaning.

**Best Features:** Easy to use, can be for any issue, can be done anywhere, improves with practice, and can affect body, mind and emotions.

**Possible Shortcomings**: Effect may be too subtle for some. Alternately, it could be too powerful or nauseating for others. Also, it does not necessarily lead to spiritual maturity, it can take a while to learn what works for you, and each crystal costs money.

# CHAPTER 32

# THE CHEERFUL CHANTER

In the Western world, not many people think of chanting as a top tier method for feeling joy. Yet, in the world at large it's a different story. From Muslims reading the Qur'an out loud, to Buddhists, Hindus, or Christians singing repetitive songs, chanting has been a popular tool for feeling joy for several thousands of years. Anytime a method for experiencing joy or joy has been around for several thousand years, it probably means it's very effective. In fact, you have probably experienced chanting, even if you think that you haven't. Many churches have call and response prayers or simple songs that are really chants. In addition, many sports enthusiasts partake in the joys of singing easy songs with their fellow participants.

Many years ago, I had a very negative view of people who "did chanting." I associated it with vacant eyed New Agers who thought they were doing some useful spiritual practice, when it seemed to me they were just joying themselves out. Then I realized that there is nothing wrong with "joying yourself out," especially if you can do it without incurring negative side effects. Later, I met people who told me chanting had changed their life. Well, it has *not* changed my life, but nowadays I do appreciate its power. If you haven't experienced the joy of chanting alone or in a group, well—you're really missing something. Chanting can be a wonderful way to tune into a feeling of collective unity with a group of people, and a great way to dive into feelings of love, joy, peace, and devotion.

There are many different types of chanting just like there are many different types of food. Just because you don't enjoy broccoli doesn't mean you won't enjoy a good pizza. In a similar way, just because you don't appreciate the Hare Krishna chant doesn't mean you won't love a good sports team chant—or singing "Amazing Grace." Your mission, should you decide to accept it, is to seek out and find the type of chant that you find fun, joyous, meaningful, and just right for you. This may take some time and exploration.

Once I got over my initial reservations about chanting, I found that I started to love it more and more. I began with simple spiritual chants in English by a wonderful musician named John Astin (you can look him up in iTunes). Then I got into chants in Sanskrit and other languages by people such as Krishna Das and Deva Premal. While it was weird at first to sing repetitive songs that I didn't understand, after a while I found it freeing. The fact that I didn't understand the words helped me to let go of my intellect and instead focus on the *feeling* of a chant. Soon, *I* became one of those vacant eyed joyed out people who "does chanting."

Singing spiritual chants by yourself or while accompanying a favorite musician can be quite wonderful, but chanting in a group is often even more powerful. The feeling of connecting with like-minded people in a song of passion is one of the true joys every human being should know. I even like the chants that happen in sports stadiums. Whether it be singing, "We will, we will rock you!" or "Take me out to the ballgame," sports chants have their own unique flavor that is wonderful to experience.

Besides the inherent power in saying or singing repetitive words, some people feel chants can elicit their own form of spiritual energy. To begin with, the words may strike a chord in your heart just from their inherent meaning—such as in the words to "Amazing Grace," or the "Jesus Prayer." Yet, according to some, the words may invoke the energy of a spiritual being (for instance, Jesus, Krishna, the Buddha) who the chant is directed at. Rather than tell you my opinion about this, I'll leave it to you to explore this phenomena and decide for yourself.

As with many of the finer things in life, tuning into the joy, devotion, or power of a chant is somewhat of a learned skill. Give yourself time to discover and dive deeply into this tool for opening up your heart and spirit. At times, you may feel embarrassed or even stupid, but those feelings soon pass. With practice, you can learn to "surf" a chant into a place inside yourself that is both profound and ecstatic. May you enjoy the ride!

**Best Suited** for improving your Engagement, Pleasure, and Meaning.

**Best Features:** Effect can be powerful, no negative effects, low cost, improves with practice, and can lead to spiritual maturity.

**Possible Shortcomings:** Can take a while to feel, can't be done most places, very visible to others, and some folks don't enjoy it.

# CHAPTER 33

# EMF'S AND ENERGETIC SHIELDING

Now that we are firmly in the section of the book called "alternative energy methods," or as my Dad used to say, "Weird stuff," let's look at another controversial area: EMF's and energetic "shielding." I used to think that people who claimed they were feeling electromagnetic fields (EMF's) were on a par with the people who said they were abducted by aliens. Yet, a friend of mine who is sensitive to these fields proved that I was mistaken. She could *consistently* tell me if my smartphone or Wi-Fi router were turned on or not. When they were on, she felt weak. When they were turned off, she felt fine.

So that we can have an intelligent discussion about this controversial subject, let me first give you some scientific background. There are natural EMF's that are produced by both the human body and the Earth itself. Yet, now there are also a host of "artificial EMF's" that come from everything from cell phones, to microwave ovens, to Wi-Fi routers, to high voltage wires. These artificial EMF's have been shown to disturb the human body's natural energetic field if supplied in high enough doses. Unfortunately, we are currently exposed to 100 million times greater artificial EMF radiation than our grandparents were. Depending upon who you ask, this is either not a problem—or a potential catastrophe in the making.

This being America, every opinion about this issue is readily found on the Internet. Yet, I think it's safe to say that some people strongly feel the impact of these forms of electromagnetic radiation—whether they realize the source of it or not. Personally, I never thought I was impacted by such things. Yet, historically I've noticed that whenever I spend a long time on a plane, I tend to feel weak and drained. When a friend of mine told me that planes are like "intense EMF cages that suck your energy," I was intrigued. I bought a couple of gadgets that supposedly reduce the impact of EMF radiation, and lo and behold, I no longer feel drained when on long plane flights. Placebo effect? Maybe. But the effect is not subtle. Whereas it used to take me a quite a while to recover from a long plane flight, now I'm good to go right off the plane.

If you suspect that you may be sensitive to EMF radiation, there are some simple (and not so simple) things you can do. First, the not so simple: You can live in a cave in the Himalayas, or find a home in a remote location that does not get cell reception. Good luck finding that. Fortunately, there are simpler things you can do. You can try to avoid Wi-Fi whenever possible by using an Ethernet cable. In addition, you can buy various gadgets that can help. These gadgets range in price from about $3 to about $3000. As with all unregulated health gadgets, you need to be careful that you're not just throwing away your money. A good web site to learn more is: www.electricsense.com.

I'm not an EMF fanatic. By that I mean I think it's a good idea to avoid exposure to high intensity EMF fields if it's easy to do or doesn't cost much. Fortunately, I've found some common sense ideas and good products that seem to do just that. Perhaps the easiest thing you can do is to put any Wi-Fi router you have in your house at least 10 feet away from where you put your body. These magic gizmos put out a lot of EMF waves, and if you spend hours a day near one, it's like living in a microwave oven. Speaking of microwave ovens, when cooking something, stay a few feet away. Even with the oven doors closed, a lot of EMF leaks out.

A second way to easily avoid EMF waves is to put a laptop "radiation screen" on your laptop. You can buy one of these for about $75, and if you suspect that your laptop is making you sick and tired (instead of your work), then this can be a good investment. The "HARApad Elite 2.0" gets good reviews. You can buy it and/or read its technical reviews (along with the reviews of many other good products) at www.lessemf.com.

A third way to protect yourself from "bad energy" and EMF radiation is to buy a pendant that you wear around your neck. It's harder to measure the effectiveness of these types of devices, yet many people (and scientific research) report good experiences with them. There are literally hundreds of these types of pendants, but to save you time, I'll recommend a couple. First is something called the "Q-link." You can buy one of these for about $100 at www.qlinkproducts.com. Their website is filled with scientific research, mumbo-jumbo, and lots of different models. Generally, the reviews are quite good. If you're willing to wear a pendant, the Q-link is probably a good bet.

Two other products worth mentioning are the Aires shield, which will only run you about $50 at www.toolsforwellness.com. (Click on EMF protection to see a full list of products). From what I hear, all the Aires products are pretty great and have a bunch of research backing up their claims. Or, if you're looking for something that gets the best rave reviews, try any of the Earthcalm.com devices for EMF protection. When I put on one of Earthcalm's pendants (about $250), my *toes* actually got a lot warmer. For my whole life, I've had cold toes, but as soon as I wore one of these pendants, bang! My toes felt warm for the first time in my life. I can't say their pendant protected me from EMF waves, but it surely was doing something to my body.

While I've focused on how these products can help with EMF protection, many people report feeling stronger, happier, and healthier when wearing a pendant. We are made up of energy. If we can protect ourselves from harmful energy, it makes sense that we'll feel better. So if you suspect that you may be sensitive to EMF radiation or other potentially harmful energy, it's worth a shot. Who knows, at the very least you may end up with much warmer toes.

**Best Suited** for increasing Pleasure and Accomplishment.

**Best Features:** Easy to use, no negative effects, invisible, can be done anywhere.

**Possible Shortcomings:** Effect may be subtle, gadgets can be expensive, doesn't lead to greater maturity.

# CHAPTER 34

# THE LIGHT THAT MAKES THINGS RIGHT

I am not a morning person. I wake up groggy no matter how much sleep I get, and historically it has taken me awhile to feel fully alert. As a psychotherapist, I was aware that some of my patients benefitted from what is sometimes referred to as "Light therapy." Such therapy is usually prescribed for people who suffer from something called Seasonal Affective Disorder, often referred to as the "winter blues" or S.A.D. for short. In essence, "Light therapy" consists of sitting in front of a special light for about 30 minutes a day—usually in the morning. Well, I don't seem to have S.A.D., but I wondered if such a light might help me feel better in the morning—so I recently purchased one.

For somewhere between $40 and $150 bucks, you can get a "Lightbox." On Amazon.com there are a lot of reviews of the various options. The research on the effectiveness of Lightboxes is actually quite impressive. According to Wikipedia, "Controlled-trial comparisons with antidepressants shows equal effectiveness, with less expense and more rapid onset of therapeutic benefit." In addition, Lightboxes aren't usually associated with any negative side effects. Yet, since I don't suffer from Seasonal Affective Disorder, I didn't really know if there would be any benefit for me. Thus, I conducted a little "experiment."

For one week I rated how good I felt 30 minutes after I woke up, and an hour after I woke up. Then, the following week I used a Lightbox for 30 minutes upon awakening. I simply sat at my computer with the light shining on me while I read the New York Times on the Internet and ate my breakfast. Then I rated how I felt immediately after the "light treatment," and once again 30 minutes later. Wow, what a difference! The week that I sat in front of the Lightbox, I felt significantly better, had more energy, felt more joyous, and was much more alert and productive in the morning. I became a Lightbox evangelist.

In our society, there's a lot of effort put into helping people who feel terrible to feel normal. Yet, there's very little discussion of how to help "normal" people to feel even better. Although I had suggested Lightboxes to some of my patients who suffer from depression, it had never occurred to me that *I* might benefit from one. To my surprise, it made quite a difference—both in helping me wake up in the morning and in helping me feel more energized during the day.

To get a sense of how "Light therapy" may be of help to you, I can offer you a four minute video on YouTube that can give you a taste. Here is the URL you can find it at: https://www.youtube.com/watch?v=uzuAXLF6Hbw.

This video was made by my friend Dr. Norman McVea. He has an assortment of innovative products that subtly help people experience expanded states of consciousness. In this brief video, Dr. McVea created a specialized flashing light video with mind altering sounds that is geared towards waking people up quickly. To get the most benefit from it, just make the video full screen, turn up the light intensity on your computer, turn up your speakers, and then stare at the images for 4 minutes. If you're like me, you'll notice this video quickly "wakes up" your brain. I call it e-coffee. To learn more about Dr. McVea's innovative sound and light products, you can go to his website www.CoherentCoachingInstitute.com. There's a wealth of info on this site, and if you put in your email address he'll update you as new products become available.

I'm really glad I discovered the wonders of Light therapy. It has made my mornings more joyous, and given me more energy than even a cup of coffee. In addition, with Light therapy there's no "crash" at the end. For a little bit of money, maybe this underutilized technology can work its magic on you too.

**Best Suited** for increasing Pleasure, Engagement, and Accomplishment.

**Best Features**: Easy to use, quick, effective, no negative side effects, and can affect the body, mind, and emotions.

**Possible Shortcomings:** Cost (although the video is free), doesn't deal with underlying issues, can't be done anywhere, does not improve with practice, and does not lead to greater maturity.

# CHAPTER 35

# GIVE PEACE A CHAIR

After going to the first annual Transformational Technology conference in October of 2015, I met some folks who told me about a "magical chair" that induced deep meditative experiences. For me, such rumors were like telling an alcoholic about a hidden bottle of fine wine. Eventually I tracked down the alleged magical chair, and talked to its creator, Dr. Dan Cohen. Dr. Cohen had previously licensed and launched the Breathe Right® nasal strip that many athletes use, and are now found in almost every drug store around the country. As a doctor interested in helping himself and others experience states of consciousness beyond ego, he worked for many years to create a chair that would facilitate such a process. The result is something called the " SolTec Lounge."

According to their web site, www:ToolsToAwaken.com, "SolTec technology consists of amplified layered music played through transducers that generate music and vibration in addition to synchronized electromagnetic fields. This results in physical, emotional, mental and spiritual changes that diminish the influence of the ego, while enhancing states of peace and relaxation." In plain English, this means you sit in the chair for 20 to 50 minutes, do nothing, and the chair does stuff to you that results in very interesting experiences and states of consciousness.

I drove four hours to a friend's place that had recently obtained such a chair—just so I could have some first hand experience with it. My friend set me up for a 50 minute session by putting some headphones on my head, showing me a couple of knobs for controlling the intensity, and then said I should do nothing—in fact, feel free to go to sleep. The "chair" is more like a comfortable recliner, and in fact has the ability to recline much like a dentist's chair. The first thing I noticed as I relaxed into the recliner was that the entire thing vibrated to the music coming in on the headphones. It was pleasant, but nothing profound. Yet, as I lay there, I began to feel deeply relaxed. The relaxation felt different than just having my muscles relax. It felt like my individual *cells* were relaxing—like my energy field was being suffused in a bathtub of gentle euphoria.

To my surprise, as the experience progressed, it went through various stages. My 50 minute "ride" ranged from mild euphoria to brief physical discomfort, to pulsing energy, to twilight sleep, to deep bliss. At the end of the session, onlookers immediately asked me, "So how was it?" At that moment, I realized that my desire and/or ability to speak was practically at zero. I was simply too relaxed physically and energetically to put words together in a coherent manner. After a bit, I mumbled some words, but the effect lasted quite awhile even after I peeled myself away from the chair.

Next, a friend of mine also tried the chair. Yet, her experience was quite different than my own. Rather than the energetic opening and euphoria I felt, her chair experience resulted in her "brain feeling different." Indeed, as I talked with various people who had used the chair, the range of experiences I heard about was vast. The only similarity seemed to be that by the end of the session, no one felt like they wanted to make the effort to put words to the experience. Dr. Cohen explained this variety of experience by saying the chair was not attempting to induce a specific experience. Instead, according to Dr. Cohen, the goal of the chair was to facilitate an energetic shift that each individual needed at the moment they used the chair.

As I talked to people who had used the chair a lot of times, I was interested in knowing how their sessions with the chair "progressed." I was pleased to hear that, for the most part, the sessions seemed to get deeper. As I've noted throughout this book, with some "joy inducing modalities," a quick tolerance effect seems to happen. The more you use it, the less effective it seems to become. However, this was not what people reported as they repeatedly used this chair. As people used this recliner over time, it seemed to facilitate an ever deepening energetic opening.

According to Dr. Cohen, an important goal of using the chair "is achieved when your level of awareness increases such that you are able to realize the difference between your higher self and your egoic or lower mind." Dr. Cohen believes that, as a species, we need to learn how to transcend our egoic mind and all the trouble it causes us. By having a chair or other method that helps us tune into our higher mind or higher self, we will be able to create a more harmonious life. If enough people used such methods to tune into their higher mind, maybe we could even create world peace. When Dr. Cohen asked me for a good advertising slogan for the chair, I suggested, "Give Peace a Chair." He loved it. Being that I'm a pretty lazy person, I love the idea of a chair that, by simply lying in it, facilitates an awakening to one's higher mind. This chair seems to be an impressive candidate for such an outcome.

I was pleasantly surprised to hear that the chair only costs $3200 plus shipping. While not cheap, that's not bad for a chair that induces deep physical and even spiritual experiences. I have an office chair that

I paid $1500 for, and although it's quite comfy, it has never induced a spiritual experience in me. In addition to the $3200 SolTec Chaise, Dr. Cohen is now working on an even more powerful (and more expensive) version. Although I haven't personally tried it, I have talked to people who have said it's even much more intense. Who knows what the future holds. In a few years, maybe everyone will be singing, "All we are saying, is give peace a chair."

**Best Suited** for increasing Pleasure, Engagement, and Meaning.

**Best Features**: Easy to do, powerful, can affect the body, mind, and emotions, improves with practice, and may lead to greater maturity.

**Possible Shortcomings**: Cost, takes a fair amount of time to use, and may lead to unpleasant experiences in some people.

# SECTION SIX

# THE BODY AND BEYOND

In Western culture, we tend to think of the body, the mind, and the spirit as separate entities. In reality, everything is interconnected. For example, if your body doesn't feel good, it's easier to fall into negative thought patterns. The good news is that, if you can do something wonderful for your body, your mind, emotions, and spirit will likely benefit too. In this section, I'll explore several of my favorite ways to dramatically impact one's body. Not only do these modalities feel good to one's body, they can also positively impact all the other aspects of you.

In a day and age where we often spend hours a day sitting and looking at a computer screen, our bodies can use all the help they can get. Fortunately, there are a lot of great products out there to remedy our bodily woes. Whenever possible, I try to focus on products or tools that are not widely known, and are free or low-cost. However, I have made an exception on three of the products in this section. The "floatation tank," the "far infrared sauna," and massage chairs all cost a lot of money. However, it is possible to rent them by the hour for a small amount of money in most cities.

As with the other items I've reviewed, you will need to experiment and see what works for you. Once you find something you love, I suggest you create a ritualized way of keeping it in your life. My wife has done this by going to a "Five Rhythms" dance class a couple times a week, and I wake up each morning with a brief "Tinger" scalp massage. Once such a ritual is established, you can reap the benefits without having to struggle to remember to use your life enhancing method. Have fun exploring, and good luck.

# CHAPTER 36

# FOOT AND HAND MASSAGING

Recently, a friend asked me to name my top ten ways of finding joy. It's an interesting exercise to do—both for yourself and your loved ones. I was surprised to realize that hand and foot massage made my top ten list. It also made my wife's top ten list, which is probably why most nights we trade hand and foot massages while we talk about our days. It's a great way to relax and nurture each other, and it has the added benefit of being good for our health and sending our endorphin levels through the roof.

In the last decade, foot massage has gotten a foothold (I couldn't help myself!) in America. You can now find spas throughout the USA that advertise "Foot Massage—Walk-Ins Welcome." However, in places like China, the art of foot massage (aka reflexology) has been around for thousands of years. When I was in China, I noticed that I never seemed to be more than 100 yards from a foot massage business. For about $4 an hour, I was a very happy camper when I was in China. Fortunately, since our feet and hands are conveniently located on our very own body, you can massage *your own* feet and hands. Of course, it's not as delightful as having them massaged *for* you, but the price is certainly right. Anything that's free, feels great, is easy to do, and is good for you is a real find. No wonder it's on my top ten list.

If you don't want to massage your own feet or hands, and you don't have a partner you can persuade to do it for you, there are various gadgets you can buy. These gadgets range from $3 wooden foot rollers to $350 electronic foot and calf massagers. In general, you get what you pay for. If you're thinking of getting one, it's a good idea to try it out first. Each gadget does different things, and if you're spending a lot of money, you want to make sure it has the feel you really want. Brookstone store (located in many airports) and Bed, Bath, and Beyond often have some good foot massagers you can try out in the store. Your next best bet is to type in "foot massagers" or "hand massagers" at Amazon.com and see what people recommend at various price ranges.

Although I am clearly a gadget guy, I want to put in a plug (or maybe take *out* a plug) for skin-to-skin contact. No machine –no matter how expensive—can do what a caring human being can do. The feet and hands are inundated with acupuncture points that can only be fully stimulated with the human hand. Besides, people crave skin-to-skin contact, and massage of one's feet and/or hands is a great way to share in the gift of touch—without the need for birth control.

If you want to learn how to do a good foot or hand massage (for yourself or a friend), you can find plenty of tips on the Internet. Just Google, "How to give a foot massage" or a similar phrase at Youtube. com. Another (low tech) way to become skilled at this art form is to simply practice on yourself. You'll soon see what works well—and what does not. Or, if you have a partner you plan to trade massages with, you might try the following exercise: Ask your partner to give you constant feedback about your massage as you give them your best effort. For example, as you massage their foot, they can say numbers from one to ten, with "one" indicating that what you're doing hurts or feels unpleasant, to "ten" representing that they're in heaven. Within a few minutes of doing this exercise, you'll quickly learn what kind of pressure and touch your partner most desires.

If you don't want to explore the old fashioned way of giving or receiving a foot massage, there are a couple of gadgets I can heartily recommend. If money is no object, then treat yourself to the Human Touch Modern Reflex 2 Calf and Foot Massager. At about $260 bucks, it does a nice job. Some people say it's the next best thing to skin-to-skin contact. If money is tight, you can do no wrong with buying a HoMedics FMS-200H Shiatsu Elite Foot Massager for about $50.

As far as hand massagers go, there is basically only one style on the market. It's a Breo ipalm520 Acupressure Hand Massager. It sells for about $138. Some people like these, some don't. I thought it was pretty good, but I'm a slut when it comes to any kind of massage. In Chapter 40 I talk about acupressure rings. These can be picked up for about $2 each, and almost everyone I know likes these handy gadgets. They are not electronic, but they do make the massage of your fingers a lot easier and more enjoyable than would otherwise be. As an added bonus, acupressure rings can also be used on one's toes. Highly recommended.

One of the great things about getting regular foot or hand massage is the fact that your feet and hands become more *sensitive* to their massages. When I first experienced foot and hand massages, I enjoyed them, but they were no big deal. Yet, after 30 years of frequent massage, my feet and hands are now ultra-sensitive. I can literally feel my brain be overwhelmed with endorphins as my feet or hands are massaged. No matter how hard a day I've had, I know that great pleasure and joy are only a couple of feet (pun intended) away—conveniently located at the end of my own appendages. How cool is that?

**Best Suited** for increasing Pleasure and Engagement.

**Best Features**: Easy to do and learn, free (to do on yourself), quick and effective, no negative effects, improves with practice, and can affect the body, mind, and emotions.

**Possible Shortcomings:** Electric massagers cost money, you can't do this anywhere, doesn't deal with root issues, and does not lead to greater maturity.

# CHAPTER 37

# THE ISOLATION FLOAT TANK

According to the New York Times, isolation float tanks "have become increasingly popular tools to combat pain and reduce stress." In case you haven't heard of these contraptions, isolation float tanks are nine-foot long fiberglass "coffin-shaped" pods filled with skin temperature salt water. When lying in them, the salt water helps you to float, and the warmness of the water and blackness of the tank make it so you experience no external bodily sensations. They were invented by Dr. John Lilly back in 1974, but they have gone in and out of popularity since the 70's. Nowadays, they are experiencing a renaissance, where people pay $30 to $100 for a ninety minute session in hundreds of "floatation locations" around the country.

I used to live at a house that had its own float tank—so I have a lot of experience with them. They take a little getting used to, but once you learn to relax into the environment (or lack thereof), you're free to examine your mind in a new way. After all, there are no visuals, sound, or sensations, so what you're left with is your inner dialogue—or perhaps a glimpse of the peace within. Whenever I would use the "tank," I would come out feeling relaxed and refreshed, as well as humbled by how active my mind usually is.

Isolation tanks have been shown to be effective in taking people from a "beta" brain wave state to a "theta" state. Theta is often associated with an increased ability to problem solve and/or be creative. In Silicon Valley and other high stress places, many people use tanks as a way to unplug from the world of stimulation and tap into their creative brain. People usually love them or hate them, and you never know which category you'll fall into until you try it.

Recently, I went to visit Glen and Lee Perry, the people who make Samadhi tanks—the major player in the field. The Perry's have been making tanks for about 40 years, and told me, "The growth right now is extremely rapid." Glen said he sees the tanks as a useful tool because they act like "a magnifying glass for your mind." I would agree. Without outward stimulation, you can better see what your mind thinks, how it operates, and how certain practices (like meditation methods) affect what your mind does. While I was in their tank, I got new insights about how to more effectively use a "letting go" method I use daily. When I left the tank, I felt very refreshed.

Because you float in an isolation tank, many people report it helps them to reduce the symptoms of stress or chronic pain they experience. Other people use it to explore how various legal and illegal drugs affect their mind and body. Since the tank frees you of any external input, it is an effective way to magnify or witness your emotions and your inner dialogue. Depending upon what your emotions or inner dialogue are doing, this could be very pleasant—or somewhat unpleasant.

If this description here intrigues you, your next step is to Google "floatation locations" and find the nearest rentable tank near you. For about the price of a massage, you can have a unique inward journey.

Generally, after a single session you'll know if a floatation tank feels more like a doorway to the Kingdom of Heaven within, or more like a coffin. Either way, I'm sure you'll find it to be an interesting experience.

**Best Suited** for increasing a sense of Meaning and Pleasure.

**Best Features:** Can affect the body, mind, and emotions in a powerful way, and can lead to greater spiritual maturity.

**Possible Shortcomings:** Cost, difficult to use, can't be done anywhere, can sometimes be unpleasant, and is not quick.

# CHAPTER 38

# THE CLARITY OF AROMATHERAPY

I used to think of aromatherapy was one of those things "new age" people do when they're not busy talking to angels. It just seemed a bit too woo-woo for me. Then a friend of mine gave me some essential oils as a gift. She told me to rub a couple of drops on my wrists and then take three deep inhalations of the oil. The bottle said the word "Breathe" on it, so I figured it was safe. Well, I immediately felt better—much better. Not only was I breathing deeper, but a nice warm feeling of vitality swelled up within me. Then my friend gave me "dessert." She had me breathe in a couple of drops from a bottle called "Wild Orange." It immediately made me feel happy. I was hooked.

According to Wikipedia, "Aromatherapy uses plant materials and aromatic plant oils, including essential oils, and other aromatic compounds for the purpose of altering one's mood, cognitive, psychological, or physical well-being." It's been around in one form or another for thousands of years. Our olfactory sense is very primal. If you stimulate it in just the right way, it can make you feel wonderful and help you remember great memories from the past. Obviously, the perfume industry knows that the right scent can lead to attraction and sexual desire, and the same is true for certain essential oils too.

In doing a bit of research about aromatherapy, I learned some very useful practical tips. First of all, there are a lot of different types of oils, from straight oils like peppermint and eucalyptus, to mixtures that include several oils mixed in to create a specific effect. For example, there are concoctions made to stimulate your body, help you recover from stress, help you with breathing, lift you up from depression, or even help you go to sleep. If you have any psychological or physical affliction, you can probably find an aromatherapy bottle made to be of help. Since the qualities of these products can differ quite a bit, I find it helpful to look up reviews on Amazon.com to get a sense of how satisfied people are with specific products.

Although I am no aromatherapy expert, I've found the "Doterra" product line to be of top-notch quality. I have especially enjoyed their "Breathe" and "Wild Orange" mixtures, but also like "Balance," "Ylang Ylang," and "Lime." They have so many different oils, that there are too many to mention here. Besides, everyone is different. It's best to find a place that sells these oils and see what smells you're most attracted to. If you have a good health food store in your area, they may carry various essential oils—with "tester" bottles for you to try.

Once you find some oils or mixtures that fit in with your needs or desires, have fun experimenting with how to use them. A common way people use essential oils is to put a few drops in a bottle of massage oil. For example, lavender—an oil that's very calming to people—is frequently added to regular massage oil. You can also put a few drops in a bath, or on a damp wash cloth to rub all over your body after a shower.

For people who have sinus or bronchial problems, certain essential oils can be a Godsend. Eucalyptus and peppermint oil are especially popular for helping people to breathe better. Try adding six or so drops to a bowl of steaming hot water, then putting a towel over your head as you lean over to capture the steam. Close your eyes and inhale until the water cools. In just a couple of minutes, you'll likely feel significantly better.

Each morning when I take a shower, I put a half drop of Doterra's "Breathe" or Olbas Oil (a combination of eucalyptus and peppermint oil) in each nostril. Then I take some deep breaths. The combination of the oil and the water of the shower enlivens me and makes me more awake. I use it instead of a cup of coffee. Olbas Oil is available in a lot of health food stores, and sometimes even at CVS. A $7.00 bottle will last you a surprisingly long time. Olbas also sells an inhaler that does pretty much the same thing as the oil, and can sometimes be a bit more convenient.

Admittedly, the effect of essential oils tends to be short lived. But if you put a couple of drops on your hair or on your neck, throughout the day you can be rewarded with a whiff of your favorite fragrance. Recently, I bought a somewhat expensive bottle of rose essential oil, and found that every time I smelled its sweet scent, my heart seemed to open. Whether you're looking to brighten a good day, or lift yourself out of a stressful day, aromatherapy can be a fun and easy way to bring more joy into your life.

**Best Suited** for increasing Pleasure.

**Best Features**: Easy to use, quickness of effect, no negative effects, low cost, invisible to others, and can be done anywhere.

**Possible Shortcomings:** Effect can be subtle and short lived, and does not lead to greater emotional or spiritual maturity.

# CHAPTER 39

# THE INFRARED SAUNA EXPERIENCE

In case you haven't heard of far infrared saunas, they are a type of sauna that uses the far infrared part of the electromagnetic spectrum. The result is that they do not become as hot as regular saunas, but you actually sweat more. The infrared electromagnetic waves seep deep into your body, and relax and heat up your muscles from the inside out. If you're the type of person that gets cold easily or likes a sauna, having one of these in your living room can be a Godsend. If you type in "Far Infrared sauna" into Google, you'll find plenty of information and sauna kits that fit between one and six people.

Whenever possible, I try to review products that cost under $300. Yet here I will make an exception. I've owned a far infrared sauna for about five years. Typically they cost between $1000 and $3000. Occasionally, you can also find them in gyms and health clubs. If you don't want to spend that kind of money, you can also get some of the benefits of far infrared by buying a far infrared heating pad. Depending on size, these can cost between $90 and $500. You can find a variety of these products at www.toolsforwellness.com. Once on their site, click on "Pain Relief and General Health" to find a list of the infrared heating pads. If you have questions, the folks at Tools For Wellness are very helpful in answering your questions.

So why might it be worth your while to check out such products? Well, for one, they're really good for you. The health benefits are well documented. Secondly, they feel good. I love sitting in my sauna and having a good sweat—especially when it's cold outside.

While I enjoy my infrared sauna, my wife absolutely loves it. Recently, I asked her why she loves it so much. She said, "It relaxes me as much as a large glass of wine, makes my skin shine, and leaves me feeling refreshed for hours." That's a pretty good testimonial for something that is one of the healthiest things you can do for your body.

If you're thinking of buying a far infrared sauna, it's always a good idea to do your research. After extensive research, I settled on a two person Clearlight Infrared Sauna by Sauna Works. It cost me about $2300 installed. Some people say the $1000 saunas use inferior heaters or wood, but I don't really know. All I know is that my sauna has been great, and it requires exactly zero upkeep or maintenance. In addition, in the last five years, I've only been sick three days. I can't say for sure, but all that sweating seems to have led to a lot less sick days. In that way, the sauna can pay for itself over time.

**Best Suited** for improving your Pleasure (and health).

**Best Features:** Easy to use, powerful effect, and good for your health.

**Possible Shortcomings:** Cost, doesn't help with specific issues, can't be done anywhere, doesn't lead to greater maturity, and doesn't improve with practice.

# CHAPTER 40

# THE TINGLER AND ACUPRESSURE RINGS

A "Tingler" is the common name given to a simple hand held device for massaging one's scalp. I first became aware of "The Tingler" about 15 years ago. At the time, they cost about $20 and were made out of copper. They looked a little bit like a spider with 8 inch long copper legs. By placing these wiry "legs" over your own or someone else's scalp, a unique tingling or pleasurable sensation could be had. Some people thought the sensation was the greatest thing since sliced bread. Others found it a bit disturbing. Personally, I loved it. However, over the years, "The Tingler" has become lighter, less expensive, and remodeled to be even more effective. Nowadays, it feels so good that I am amazed that not everyone has one.

My introduction to the new and improved Tingler came at the Burning Man festival about five years ago. A couple invited me to sit in a chair and get "tingled." The man and the woman each held two Tinglers in their hands. The man placed two of the Tinglers on my scalp, and the woman placed one Tingler over each knee. What happened next blew my mind. As the couple slowly moved the four Tinglers up and down on my scalp and knees, my body exploded with pleasure. The only way I can describe it would be to say it felt like an orgasm, but even more intense. My screams of delight soon attracted other participants. Within five minutes, there was a long line of people volunteering to get "tingled."

As I watched other people get tingled, I noticed that about 10% of people didn't like it, but the other 90% were totally hooked. Once people were tingled, I would ask them to describe the sensation. A lot of people used words like "orgasm," and "the most pleasurable thing I've ever felt." About 10% of the women stated that it had induced in them an *actual* spontaneous orgasm. (Note to couples: The Tingler is the best, cheapest, and most effective sex toy I know of). Not bad for a dollar!

If you want to partake in this amazing but little known phenomena, here's all you need to know. If you go to Amazon.com and type in "head tingler" you will be given a list of sellers of various head massagers. I suggest you get the ones that are the thinnest and the cheapest. They are often referred to as "hand held scalp head massagers." Typically, they cost about one dollar each when purchased in groups of two or four. Personally, I buy them by the dozen and give them away to friends. Over the years, I've had a lot of people thank me for this simple, but enduring way to feel immense pleasure.

To get maximum benefit from your Tingler, here are a couple of things you need to know. First, while you can tingle yourself, it does not feel nearly as good as when someone else tingles you. Oh well. I think this is God's way to make sure we don't just sit around and tingle ourselves 24 hours a day! Secondly, two Tingler's on the head seem to be better than one, especially when used by an experienced practitioner. In addition, I find that moving the Tinglers slowly and randomly across your friend's scalp creates the most ecstatic moans of ecstasy.

If you have more than one person available to tingle a friend, then by all means give it a whirl. Two Tinglers on the scalp and one on each knee creates my favorite effect. Yet, placing a Tingler over each shoulder and moving them up and down slowly can also be amazingly wonderful. Like with most skills, with practice you get better at tingling your friends, and better at knowing exactly what they most enjoy.

A related little gizmo that packs a punch is what is sometimes called “acupressure rings” or “fidgets.” (You can look on Amazon.com under either name to see what I’m talking about.) These “rings” are made to go over any finger or thumb and, by pushing them up and down the finger, deeply stimulate the acupressure points. It feels wonderful, like a really good hand massage. You can also use these rings to massage your toes. As you quickly push the ring up and down each finger (or toe), you’ll notice the energy in your entire body starts to feel more balanced. It’s like a quick acupuncture session you can give to yourself—anytime and anywhere.

While Tinglers and acupressure rings may sound like simple toys for inducing brief pleasure, they also have other uses. When I get tired in the afternoon, I tingle myself briefly as a way to wake up my brain. In addition, sometimes I use the Tingler in lieu of coffee in the morning. I know other people who swear by the Tingler’s ability to cure tension headaches. As for acupressure rings, I find that they relax and balance me when I have to sit in a plane for a long time. Have fun discovering your own unique ways to tingle and balance yourself and others. At little cost and little risk of addiction, these tools pack quite a wallop.

**Best Suited** for increasing your Pleasure and Relationships.

**Best Features**: Easy to use, quick, powerful effect, low cost, can be done anywhere, no negative effects, and can be used to affect others.

**Possible Shortcomings**: Does not help with issues, does not improve with practice, and does not lead to greater maturity.

# CHAPTER 41

# ECSTATIC AND FIVE RHYTHMS DANCE

Dance has been around ever since human beings have been around. On shows such as *Dancing With the Stars*, we see couples perform amazing displays of coordination and acrobatics. It looks like fun, but we know that to dance like that would take more time and practice than we are likely to have. What to do? Fortunately, you do not have to be a "good dancer" in order to experience the joy and ecstasy of dancing. Nowadays, hundreds of cities have groups known as "Five Rhythms" or "Ecstatic Dancing" that require no skill or practice. That's my kind of dancing!

Ecstatic Dance is the easiest. According to the website ecstaticdance.org, there are only three things you need to know in order to do ecstatic dance: 1) Move however you wish. 2) No talking on the dance floor. 3) Respect yourself and one another. Depending upon what city you are in, Ecstatic Dance groups often charge between $10 and $20 to enter the dance hall. The music varies depending on the DJ, but it often has an electronic or techno feel to it. You can find a list of cities and times where ecstatic dancers gather at their web site. If you would like to try dancing with no structure whatsoever, this is the place for you. Although dancing with another person is allowed, usually Ecstatic Dance involves simply dancing and moving your body on your own.

Five Rhythms dance is similar to Ecstatic Dance, but there's more structure. People still dance on their own, but as the name implies, there are five distinct types of music played in a particular order. According to the 5Rhythms.com website, "While a seemingly simple process, the 5Rhythms practice facilitates deep and unending explorations, moving the dancer beyond self-imposed limitations and isolation into new depths of creativity and connection." The five distinct types of movement in 5Rhythms are called: Flowing, Staccato, Chaos, Lyrical, and Stillness.

In "Flowing," according to the website, "We physically practice the art of being fluid in our bodies. In Staccato, we physically practice the power of masculine energy. It is percussive and strong and promotes connection with the rest of the world. In Chaos we physically practice the art of fully releasing our bodies—we let go of the head, spine, hips and feet and move faster than we can think. In Lyrical we practice the art of coming out of Chaos. It is the physical, energetic, emotional, and spiritual dancing rebirth. (In) Stillness, we move in slow motion—like highly unpredictable meditative Tai Chi masters."

By dancing to music that facilitates each of the five different rhythms, a person is led on an inward journey of movement and meditation. Where you end up can be different each time. Sometimes I've seen people at Five Rhythms dances sobbing in deep grief, and sometimes I've seen people leaping in ecstasy. As for me, I feel deeply cleansed after dancing the Five Rhythms. All the stress and emotional stuff I have going on when I enter the dance floor tends to disappear by the time the dancing is done. In a way, such dancing can act like therapy for your body. Since the body is attached to the mind (on a good day), many

Five Rhythm dancers say it is a form of therapy for their body, mind, and soul.

As with Ecstatic Dance, 5Rhythms dance gatherings usually occur in a big room with a DJ. The cost varies, but $10 to $20 is pretty common. To find a class in your area, simply go to the 5Rhythms.com website and click on "Find a class" in the navigation bar. You can also Google "Five Rhythms + (your city)" and see what shows up. There are also a lot of four hour or one day workshops in the Five Rhythm format that can also be found on their website.

I love Five Rhythms, and so does my wife. I encourage my wife to go as often as possible because she always comes back feeling refreshed and in a good mood. If you're cheap and lazy like me, you can create your own Five Rhythms playlist by Googling "5 rhythms music playlist". You'll find some websites that offer complete playlists for free. Just play the music and dance on your own or with a couple of friends. Of course, this isn't nearly as good as dancing with a room full of people and a great sound system, but at least the price is right.

In a culture in which many of us spend multiple hours a day sitting in a chair looking at a computer screen, Ecstatic Dance and Five Rhythms are an amazing tonic. For little money, you can tap into a community of like-minded people, exercise your body, have fun, let go of stress, and perhaps enjoy states of joy and ecstasy. It's definitely worth a try.

**Best Suited** for increasing Engagement, and Pleasure.

**Best Features:** Easy to do, powerful, no negative effects, low cost, improves with practice, and can affect body, mind, and emotions.

**Possible Shortcomings:** Takes a while to do, highly visible, and can't be done anywhere.

# CHAPTER 42

# MASSAGERS AND CHI MACHINES

Being that I'm a fanatic when it comes to pursuing healthy pleasure, this book would not be complete without a review of the various massaging, swinging, thumping, and caressing machines out there. Of course, I own a slew of them. When people visit my living room, it can be embarrassing as they scan a museum's worth of various massage type gizmos. Generally, people make fun of my "hobby" of collecting such gadgets—until they try one. Then they want to know where to buy them and how much they cost. Fortunately, most of them can be had for under $120 bucks, and some for as little as $40. That's not bad when you consider a typical massage can set you back $80 or more.

I can't say I have a favorite massager. Different massagers work on different areas of the body and attempt to do different things. Yet, if money is no object, you might consider getting one of those super-duper massage chairs. Years ago, such chairs cost upwards of five grand—and weren't very good. Nowadays, you can nab a truly amazing chair with all the bells and whistles—for about two thousand bucks. Amazon.com sells a bunch of these chairs, and some of them are quite good and go for as little as $800.

One of the newest and best of the massage chairs is called the Osaki OS-4000. You can nab one for about $2500, although you can get decent imitations of one for about $1500. This beautiful machine can massage just about every part of your body simultaneously. There is something miraculous that happens when your arms, neck, shoulders, calves, buttocks, and feet are all massaged at once. There are many programs and types of massage to choose from, such as rolling, kneading, Swedish, clapping, shiatsu, and combo. In addition, this zero gravity recliner uses airbag and heating technology to make sure your limbs are treated like a king.

If you're looking for something a lot smaller or cheaper, you might go with something called a "Shiatsu massager." Typically these are kneading type portable massagers that are good at relaxing a single spot on your back or shoulders. For $40 bucks or so, these do a decent job. I would especially recommend one if you have back or shoulder problems. One of the things I like about these units is that they do not require your hands. You simply lean into them and they do their magic.

If you're looking for something to use with your hands, there are a few good units out there worth checking out. The "Thumper" is very powerful at digging into any spot that's tight, or the Jeanie Rub or Maxi-Rub ($120) will vibrate the hell (and tightness) out of any muscle they're applied to. Five or ten minutes using any of these thumping or vibrating machines can definitely increase your endorphin levels. In addition, using them on your partner can be a great way of getting kudos and warm hugs of appreciation. Trust me on this.

Next on the list of machines to bring you physical pleasure and deep relaxation are things like the Chi Machine. The Chi Machine, and similar knock offs sometimes referred to as "swingers," don't actually massage your body. Instead, you place your ankles on the six inch high machine while lying down, and they swing your legs back and forth quickly about 3 inches. This motion has been clinically proven to relax your back, reduce inflammation, and stimulate your lymphatic system. After ten minutes of swinging your legs back and forth via this device, you may find yourself with a more relaxed back, more energy, and a better state of health. You can grab a "knock off" Chi Machine for about $100, but the original is two or three times as much. Whether the original Chi Machine is truly better is hard to say.

Since we spend so much of our lives hunched over a computer, having an easy way to move our muscles around is a good idea. Unfortunately, massages can cost a good amount of money, so buying a massage gadget can be a good investment. Surprisingly, my favorite massage "gadget" is a simple $8.00 softball. I lie down on top of it and let it dig into specific back and shoulder muscles that are tight. I find this works incredibly well for me, whereas some people find the pressure a bit too intense. Yet, the lesson is if you try enough massage gadgets, you'll eventually find one that works amazingly well for you. In an age of constant stress, such a search is worth the effort.

**Best Suited** for creating more Pleasure.

**Best Features:** Ease of use, quickness, no negative effects, and can be used on others.

**Possible Weaknesses**: Only works on the body, can't be done anywhere, and cost.

# CHAPTER 43

# APHRODISIACS AND APHRODITE

Aphrodisiacs refer to any substance that, when consumed, increases sexual desire. Aphrodite was the Greek Goddess of beauty and love. With the right aphrodisiac, you can increase your chances of getting a "visit" from Aphrodite—or at least the experience of beauty and love "she" brings. The question is, "Do aphrodisiacs really work, and if so which ones?" There is no simple answer to that. Double blind placebo controlled studies are very expensive to do. Furthermore, aphrodisiacs are not patented pharmaceuticals, therefore no one has an interest in spending millions of dollars to do a good study on aphrodisiacs. Yet over time there have been enough people—and *some* studies—to have a sense of what probably works—and what does not.

First, when talking about aphrodisiacs, the best one is the one between your ears. If you can get yourself into a sexy mood—through lighting, rituals, music, smells, clothing—whatever—then you are more likely to get a visit from Aphrodite. In fact, a large part of what makes aphrodisiacs work is the ritual of taking them. Even if an herb has no scientific backing showing that it increases sexual desire, the placebo effect is very real. If you think something will increase your sexual desire, and you subsequently ingest it, then it will likely turn you on.

Next, there are various substances that don't consistently increase sexual *desire*, but they can *decrease* sexual inhibition. These include things like alcohol, marijuana, GHB, MDMA (better known as XTC), and other drugs. There are also things, such as Viagra and a supplement by the great name of Horny Goat Weed that can help with erections. Yet, neither Viagra nor Horny Goat Weed actually increase sexual desire. However, if a man has a good, hard erection, he'll probably want to use it if a willing female is available!

There are also various foods that have been linked with increased sexual desire. For example, spicy foods that get you hot and can increase your heart rate have sometimes been called aphrodisiacs. They don't actually increase sexual desire, but they can mimic the effects of sexual attraction—and thereby help you feel sexy. Chocolate is another food often associated with sexual desire. Yet, its effects are probably due to the fact that eating chocolate feels sensuous, and feels pretty great—two things associated with sex.

Having said all these disclaimers, I'm now ready to briefly tell you about three aphrodisiacs that science backs up. In addition, the three I've listed are all relatively inexpensive and easy to get in America. Of course, as with all supplements, your reaction to them will be based on your unique body composition.

**1. Tongkat Ali**: This root has long been used as an aphrodisiac and remedy for age-related sexual disorders. According to Dr. Edward Group, "The root contains compounds that have repeatedly been shown in animal studies to stimulate libido, promote semen quality, and even support muscle growth. These effects have largely been attributed to increases in testosterone." He goes on to report that, "A separate double-blind, placebo-controlled study found that men who consumed tongkat ali on a daily basis experienced improvements in erectile function, libido, and semen volume."

If you're a guy thinking you may have low testosterone levels or you know you have low libido, daily supplementation with Tongkat Ali can be a really good thing. I recommend the stuff sold at Dr. John Gray's website, MarsVenus.com. Click on "Store" then "Health" to find a bunch of supplements that can help with libido and health.

**2. Yohimbe**: Yohimbe is used to arouse sexual excitement, for erectile dysfunction (ED), sexual problems caused by medications for depression called selective-serotonin reuptake inhibitors (SSRIs), and general sexual problems in both men and women. Recommended dosages range from 15 to 30 mg a day. Scientific research indicates that Yohimbe increases blood flow to the penis and vagina. Its stimulating effect also leads many people to feel it enhances their sexual desire. It's available online or at many health food stores.

3. **Maca:** According to folk belief, Maca is a plant known for its legendary ability to deliver energy, mental clarity, and enhance sex drive for more than 2,000 years. Due to it not being a patented drug, scientific evidence on its effectiveness is limited. Yet, some studies suggest it definitely works in animals, and has been shown to relieve symptoms of menopause in women. Recommended dosages are around 2400 mg a day.

Because sexual desire and what people find "sexy" is such an individual thing, feel free to experiment on yourself for what is an aphrodisiac for you. Many people find certain foods to be aphrodisiacs for them. This is possibly due to their sensual feel or taste, or the fact that eating or drinking them is often followed by making love (a glass of wine, anyone?). So while research may say that product X is not a real aphrodisiac, if it turns you on, then that's all that matters.

**Best Suited** for increasing Pleasure and Relationships.

**Best Features**: Easy, quick, and invisible to others.

**Possible Shortcomings:** Effect is subtle, cost, does not improve with practice, and does not lead to greater maturity.

SECTION SEVEN

# INCREASING YOUR JOY I.Q.

"They grow up too fast."

# CHAPTER 44

# MIXING, MATCHING, AND MONOTONY

In my discussion and review of these 101 tools for creating more joy, I have not talked about how one might do several of them at the same time. Partly, this is because I think it's best to try each of them on their own—at least at first. Yet, once you're experienced with a specific tool, it's up to you how you might want to mix and match them for even greater effect. Over the years, I have done a fair amount of "mixing and matching," so I can give you some broad recommendations and warnings on the topic.

First, mixing and matching happens all the time in our pursuit of enjoyable experiences. Take the tried and true joy seeking behaviors of sex, drugs, and rock n roll. Although they each can be great fun on their own, joining all three of them together can sometimes be a lot more fun. Anyone who has had a drink of alcohol and then went to a party or spent time with friends knows the joy of mixing and matching. Anyone who has had some alcohol and then enjoyed driving fast knows that it's possible to be really stupid about how you go about mixing and matching.

As previously discussed, people can react pretty differently to each of the tools I reviewed in this book. When mixing and matching, it's even harder to predict what the outcome will be. Therefore, I suggest starting out conservatively so you can avoid potentially unpleasant experiences. Yet, if you don't try stuff, you may miss out on the holy "magical combination" that sends you over the rainbow. So, ultimately I suggest you put on your "mad scientist hat" and see what interesting experiences you can concoct from the tools listed in this book.

From my mixing and matching experience, I can suggest a few do's and don'ts. First, mixing and matching is usually pretty safe except when you're dealing with drugs or supplements. Drugs and certain supplements tend to last a long time, so if you're combining them with other tools, you could be in for a "bad trip." Also, you need to be especially careful when using multiple drugs or supplements at the same time. Unless you can find research on the Internet that suggests that taking X pill with Y pill is okay, it's better to just stick with one drug or supplement at a time. That even means it's best to refrain from coffee if you're experimenting with a cognitive enhancer.

A good rule of thumb for successful mixing and matching is to join tools that might attend to different aspects of your being. For example, cognitive enhancers work primarily on one's mind. Therefore, it might be interesting to see how it affects your using the Full Release Method—which works mostly on ones emotions. Or an orgone accumulator works mostly on one's body. It could be interesting to see how that might increase the power of the Thync neurostimulator—which works via one's brain.

Of course, you're also welcome to try maximizing a single modality by using several tools that attend to the body at the same time. I have enjoyed many moments of ecstasy by being "Tingled" while in my infrared sauna, while having my feet massaged by the Genie massager.

True, it's indulgent, but there are no negative side effects from this onslaught of pleasure—and it makes me very happy.

Another advantage of mixing and matching is that it can help you avoid the problem of "tolerance." If you partake of some joy inducing pills or products on a fairly regular basis, they can become less enjoyable or effective over time. Take caffeine for example. If you drink coffee frequently, it gradually loses its ability to really stimulate you. In the same way, if you play the same video game over and over, you may find it feels monotonous after a while. On the other hand, *some* joy inducing methods just keep getting better over time. That's why one of my criteria for evaluating any method is "does it improve with practice?" I have found that several of the modalities discussed in this book get more and more enjoyable each time I use them.

Finally, when mixing and matching, it's helpful to think of the analogy of cooking. When first learning to cook, you have no idea what goes with what. Yet, with experience, you kind of intuitively learn that "liver flavored ice cream" probably wouldn't work for you. In a similar vein, as you become more familiar with what each of these tools do for you individually, you may get an intuitive "hit" as to what other technique, app, or pill may make it even better. Trust your instincts, and enjoy experimenting.

# CHAPTER 45

## HOW TO KNOW IF A TECHNOLOGY IS YOUR FRIEND

### BY ARJUNA ARDAGH AND JONATHAN ROBINSON

Living in a fast paced tech savvy world, we tend to assume that technology is our friend. Not many people would easily give-up their Google searches for perusing The *Yellow Pages* or the local library. Yet, in order to know if a *specific* technology is truly your friend, you need to be able to clearly see its precise effects on *your* life. Technology affects people in different ways—in the same way that alcohol is a fun way to relax for some people, and an addictive hell for others.

In this book, 101 different "technologies" have been offered to help you feel more joy. Yet, how can you know if any given method will truly benefit your life? It's easy to simply go along with what others think and do, but that can be a recipe for disaster. In order to identify if a particular technology is a "friend" to you, we've come up with a simple method. What follows are seven questions to help you evaluate how the technology you use affects the quality of your daily life.

Yet, before reading the seven questions presented in this chapter, it's helpful to know what *you* truly value. Ultimately, we're always trying to move in the direction of what we sincerely value, but if those values aren't clearly defined, it's hard to move in the right direction. By getting clear about what really matters to you, it's easier to decide if a specific technology is helping you. For example, if your number one value in life is "love and connection," then TV is probably not your "friend" since watching TV tends to isolate people. On the other hand, Skype *may* be useful to you since it can be an effective way to connect with people you care about.

A simple exercise you can do to ascertain your values is to simply rate them on a 1 to 12 scale, with 1 being your most important value, and 12 being your least important value. What follows is a list of twelve common values people have. Try rating them from 1 to 12 so you know what is most and least important to you. Once you know this information, it will be easier for you to know if a certain technology is likely to move you in the direction of your most important values.

_____love and connection

_____wealth

_____adventure

_____power and influence

_____safety and security

_____approval/respect

_____peace of mind

_____beauty

_____spiritual growth

_____fun and play

_____ creativity

_____ efficiency/competence

Another way to know your values is to write down everything you would do with six months left to live. Once you've written this list down, ask yourself for each item on your list, "What value would that activity most fulfill?" Soon, you'll likely see a pattern to what you wrote down.

For example, you might see that the bulk of what you would do with six months left to live would be to connect with people you care about, or perhaps go on a lot of adventures. Once you have a sense about what your values really are, the questions that follow will be of even greater help.

1. **Does This Technology Bring You Closer to People, or Help Isolate You?**

   Research shows that the number one factor in creating a life of happiness is the quality of your personal relationships. Therefore, it's important to question whether or not the tech you use is bringing you closer to people. Unfortunately, 300 Facebook friends does not equal one truly good friend who you can trust will always be there for you. Technology has a way of increasing the *quantity* of our interactions, but not always the *quality*. In fact, some studies suggest that using Facebook helps make people feel more depressed.

   Recently, when I was riding a crowded subway through Vancouver, I noticed that no one was talking to each other. Instead, most people (including me) were texting on their smartphones. While texting *is* a form of connecting with people, it seemed isolating that no one was even making eye contact with the person next to them. I decided to put down my smartphone and initiate a conversation with the person next to me. We ended up having a great conversation, and it felt really good to connect with a "stranger." This experience made me realize that, even though technology is often used to connect with friends, it can still make you feel more isolated from people in general.

   If "love and connection" are a top value for you, it's important to consider if the technology you use is truly leading to quality connections versus just a *quantity* of connections. In my own case, I find I have started to use Facebook less—because it is geared more towards quantity versus quality. Yet, since people use things like Skype or Facebook in their own unique ways, you will have to judge for yourself if these tools are helping you to meet your particular values.

2. **Does This Technology Bring You Closer to Inner Peace, or Make You Feel More Stressed?**

   Last year I got a gadget called The Muse. It's a device you wear on your forehead that gives you a read-out of your brain's EEG waves on your smartphone. Its goal is to help you calm your brainwaves down so you can experience a deeper level of peace. Unfortunately, I was getting very stressed out trying to make the damn thing work properly. I thought it would bring me closer to peace, but in fact the opposite was happening.

   We tend to assume that technology is always a way to make our life easier, but that assumption is often false. Email is great to have and very efficient to use, but getting a 100 emails a day is certainly not conducive to inner peace. Technology has a way of seeming like a good idea at first, then gradually taking over our lives before we realize what hit us. That's why some friends I know take a "technology fast" one day a week. They turn off their internet and smartphone for 24 hours, and go back to living a simpler, more peaceful life. It's a step I have so far been unwilling to take, but I can appreciate its value. By asking if a specific gadget helps you towards more peace, you can hopefully make better decisions as to when and how much to use them.

3. **Does This Technology Add Depth/Joy and Happiness to Your Life, or Move You Towards Superficiality and Anxiety?**

   Ultimately, we all want a life filled with depth, meaning, and happiness. But look around you—there aren't many people who seem wildly happy over the age of five! Why is that? Well, part of the problem is that most of us spend a lot of time rushing around and feeling like we have too much to do. Although we are each responsible for the lives we create, the sheer number of choices tech gives us can certainly contribute to our feelings of overwhelm.

I love my smartphone, but I also notice that I check it habitually every few minutes. I'm not alone. The average American checks their phone 120 times a day. That means that, on average, every eight minutes we interrupt whatever we're doing to look at our smartphone. When I read this statistic, it made me wonder what effect this habit was having on my pursuit of depth and happiness. Nowadays, I try to avoid habitually glancing at my phone when I don't really need to. It has made a difference in my life. My wife used to get really pissed off when I'd look at my phone while talking to her. Now that I'm doing that (a bit) less, it's definitely made my life (and hers) more harmonious and happy.

4. **Does This Technology Make You More Conscious and Aware or More Distracted?**

   A person's level of awareness is a benchmark of both spiritual maturity and a life of harmony. We now have access to media that details everything from our global warming crisis to how the food choices we make affect people in far off lands. In general, technology makes us both more aware and more distracted. Yet, on an individual level, it can be helpful to evaluate for yourself how different technologies affect you. For me, I realized that having 500 channels of TV for a year just made me feel more distracted.

   There now exists apps that make us more aware of anything from how many calories we're eating or burning, to how stressed our breathing pattern seems to be. Used the right way, such apps can help bring awareness to parts of our lives that used to be invisible to us. However, this can get out of control. If you find that you're spending your day downloading new apps, and cleaning your IPhone from all the apps you never use (as I recently did), then you know you've gone too far.

5. **Does This Technology Make You More Compassionate, Kind, and Loving, Or More Self-Absorbed?**

   In surveys that ask people about their values, participants often state that being a loving and compassionate person is their most important value. If love and compassion are truly as important as we say they are, then we should look to see if the technology we use is helping us toward that end. Unfortunately, technology is more often geared towards making us more efficient or entertained than more compassionate or loving. Of course, one can use Google to look up "how to be more loving?" but as I write this, the number one Google search is about Whitney Houston's mentally troubled daughter. Gossip tends to be an easier sell than true spiritual development.

   Technology can indeed help make a person more loving, but it's often not the most obvious way to use a given technology. Nowadays, you can find pretty much anything online—including YouTube videos of the Dalai Lama talking about the development of compassion. Ultimately, technology gives us a sea of choices. It's our job (and struggle) to choose wisely so that we can better live the values we aspire to.

6. **Does This Technology Improve Your Health or Negatively Impact Your Health?**

   People used to believe that medical doctors held the keys to good health. The times are a changing. Nowadays, alternative medical treatments, wearable computers, online health forums, and endless health apps are always available. Having the latest information accessible to the masses seems like a good thing, but the onslaught of information can also be stressful. For instance, I used to wear a device that helped track how I was sleeping. After a couple of weeks of wearing it, I realized I was now more anxious than ever over how much sleep I was getting. I eventually gave the device away so that I could finally get a relaxing night's sleep!

When trying out the latest health app or gadget, it's important to consider if it is truly helping you make better choices—or is it simply stressing you out. Ultimately, our level of stress impacts our health as much as the amount of calories burned.

7. **Does This Technology Make You A Wiser Person or More Immature?**

   I know a friend that spent twenty years in a Zen monastery. Whenever I see him, he seems at peace, grounded, and very wise and mature. This friend was divorced several years ago, but his Zen training seems to have helped him create a harmonious new life and new marriage. On the other hand, I know a lot of young people who are always talking about (and using) the latest apps, but they seem needy and immature in their relationships. Although they have been on dozens of online arranged dates, they don't seem nearly as wise in the ways of dating and relationships as my "Zen friend."

   It can often be hard to see if a technology is helping or hindering our emotional development or level of "maturity." After all, having an abundance of dates could help you become wiser in the ways of relationships, but quantity does not necessarily lead to quality. If you don't know if something is helping you in this way, try asking a trusted friend. They can often see things you can't. Not long ago, I asked my wife if she thought our use of an app for couples was helpful. Immediately, she said, "No, it's more of a pain than it's worth." I had been thinking it was useful, but it clearly wasn't to the person I was trying to connect with.

With the 101 various apps, gadgets, tools, and supplements in this book, you have a lot of opportunities to find something that really works for you. Having these seven questions at hand can help you, over time, see if a method *really* adds to the quality of your life.

# CHAPTER 46

# THE FUTURE OF JOY

As the great Yogi Berra once said, "It's tough to make predictions, especially about the future." Yet, certain things can be said with some degree of confidence. For one, the ability to sense various aspects of human physiology will quickly get better and less expensive. This means that our capacity to measure brainwaves, heart rate variability, emotional states, stress, and other "bio-markers" will become smaller, faster, and easier. As we get more proficient at measuring such things, we'll also become better at creating change in various aspects of our experience. These "feedback loops" will eventually lead to our becoming more skilled at tapping into feelings of peace, love, and joy. Once such breakthroughs start to occur, the increased money and interest such technologies will create will lead to an acceleration of even greater breakthroughs.

According to a recent article in *Scientific American*, the U.S. loses upward of 210 billion dollars a year just from people suffering from depression. If you combine that number with other mental health disorders, plus all that we spend on entertainment, you can see that we literally spend trillions of dollars a year trying to feel better. In this book,

I've outlined many great new (and some older) technologies for feeling happier and more joyful. Yet, as with all technologies, over time these tools will become even more effective and less costly. Imagine what will happen when incredibly effective and low cost ways to feel joyful begin to enter the mass market. It will be a worldwide revolution!

In 1995, British philosopher David Pearce wrote a small book (available for free on the Internet) called, *The Hedonistic Imperative*. In it he states, "It would be easy but unwarranted simply to extrapolate past and present trends into the indefinite future. Usually, we assume without question that our descendants—however different from us in other respects—will be biologically prone to suffer negative states of consciousness. We suppose that future generations will sometimes feel distress, both subtle and crude, just as we have always done ourselves. Yet this assumption may be naïve."

Mr. Pearce goes on to state, "The neurochemical basis of feeling and emotion is rapidly being unraveled. The human genome is going to get comprehensively decoded and rewritten. In ages to come, it will become purely an issue of (post) human decision whether unpleasant modes of consciousness are generated in any form or texture whatsoever." And finally he concludes, "**...**in freeing ourselves from the nightmarish legacy of our evolutionary past we might choose to enjoy a lifetime of raw, all-consuming orgasmic joy." Indeed, in the not too distant future, we may have complete control over how much joy we experience. At that point we will need to decide if *any* form of suffering is truly useful to us anymore.

On the near term horizon, there are likely to be important breakthroughs with technologies such as Transcranial Magnetic Stimulation (TMS), Deep Brain Stimulation (DBS), Transcranial Pulsed Ultrasound (TPU), and portable Heart Rate Variability (HRV) training. Each of these technologies, (you can Google or Wikipedia them), already show promise in treating anxiety and depression, or helping normal people feel really good. It's just a matter of time before they become cheaper and easier to use and word gets out to a bigger audience.

I started this book with a quote from science fiction writer William Gibson. He once said, "The future is already here—it's just not very evenly distributed." There *already* exists good ways to zap your brain into clarity or calmness, to guide your brainwaves into deep peace, or pop a pill that leads to hyper focus or waves of joy. In this book I've tried to give you a peek into the best of what's already out there. By familiarizing yourself with these tools, you'll be in a better position to evaluate the next wave of gizmos that will be even more effective.

According to Mikey Siegel, a roboticist turned "consciousness hacker," technology will someday help awaken humanity to its deeper transcendental potential. What might that look like? It may look like more people tapping into the "heaven within" while under the influence of a gadget or healthy supplement. It may look like less drug abuse, less stress and depression, and more appearances of spontaneous joy in our culture. It may result in greater amounts of caring and kindness as folks let their joy overflow to others. It may even lead to significant cultural, religious, and political effects as people are less caught up in stress—and more available for feeling the peace within.

These are interesting times to be alive. We are in a race between forces that could destroy ourselves and the planet, and forces that could save us from such a fate. Technology accelerates both the good and the bad. It has been my hope that, through the wise use of tools to help us tap into more peace, love, and joy, we can help create a better and more sustainable world in the future. May the tools in this book help you along *your* sacred journey...

# CHAPTER 47

# FINAL WORDS OF ADVICE

Reading about joy is very different than experiencing it firsthand. If you've read a bunch of my reviews of different methods, I encourage you to try out the ones that seem to call to you the most.

In order to have a healthy body, you need to invest your time, energy, and money in eating right, exercising, and taking good care of yourself. In order to have a life filled with more joy, peace, and love, you also need to invest time, energy, and money. In this book, I've offered 101 of the best ways I know of for doing that. Now it's up to you to take the time to explore these tools. As with all explorations, some of your adventures will turn out to be duds, and some of your escapades will turn out much better than you can even imagine. Over time, you'll develop more of a reliable repertoire of ways to experience the "kingdom of heaven within."

I encourage you to tell your friends about this book. First of all, your friends will benefit from learning of new ways to experience greater joy. Secondly, by telling your friends about this book, it will help *you* to stay motivated in your quest for greater joy, and give you an opportunity to share what you've learned with each other.

Finally, I'd love to hear your feedback and be of service to you any way I can. For more information, updates, **and a free test to help you determine which of these methods might be best suited for you,** you can go to my website: TechnologyofJoy.com or FindingHappiness.com. Also, if you're interested, I offer private consultations and workshops on finding greater happiness. To learn more, feel free to visit my websites and/or contact me at my personal email address: iamjonr@aol.com

# ABOUT THE AUTHOR

Jonathan Robinson is a psychotherapist, best-selling author of ten books, and a professional speaker from Northern California. Mr. Robinson has made numerous appearances on the *Oprah* show and *CNN*, as well as other national TV talk shows. In addition, his work has appeared in *Newsweek, USA TODAY*, and the *Los Angeles Times*, as well as dozens of other publications. He has spent more than forty years studying the most practical and powerful methods for personal and professional development.

Mr. Robinson's first book, *The Experience of God*, included interviews with such notable people as the late Mother Teresa, the Dalai Lama, Deepak Chopra, and Dr. Wayne Dyer. Jonathan's second book, *The Little Book of Big Questions*, became a New York Times bestseller, as did his book *Communication Miracles for Couples*. Mr. Robinson's other books include: *Instant Insight; Real Wealth; Shortcuts to Bliss; Shortcuts to Success, The Complete Idiots Guide to Awakening Your Spirituality,* and *Find Happiness Now.*

Jonathan speaks regularly to Fortune 500 companies such as Google, Microsoft, Dell, Bank of America, Coca-Cola, and FedEx. In his public talks and workshops, Jonathan is known for providing his audiences with powerful and immediately useful information in a fun and entertaining manner. He can be reached at iamjonr@aol.com

FOR MORE INFO ABOUT JONATHAN'S BOOKS, TALKS, AND WORKSHOPS, OR FOR 45 MINUTES OF FREE AUDIO DOWNLOADS ABOUT SIMPLE METHODS TO INCREASE YOUR LEVEL OF HAPPINESS, GO TO JONATHAN'S WEBSITE: www.FindingHappiness.com

Made in the USA
San Bernardino, CA
21 November 2016